D0541493

£ independent Cambridge

A guide to, and a celebration of,
the City's best independent traders,
venues and events.

PHL
Publishing Limited

Errors and omissions

The contents and features in this publication have been compiled and published in good faith. The publisher cannot accept any liability for any claim howsoever arising, including as a result of any person acting or refraining from acting on the contents, and whether any resultant loss is direct or indirect.

ISBN-13: 978-0-9574406-1-6

Cover price £7.99

Where to buy the book

Copies are stocked at Heffers and Waterstones and many of the indies featured in the book, for a full list of stockists go to:

www.independent-cambridge.co.uk/contact/

To order copies online go to:
www.independent-cambridge.co.uk/buy/

or drop us an email at:
info@independent-cambridge.co.uk

Thank you

Thanks to everyone who supports us in our campaign to promote the fabulous range of independents in Cambridge and local area.

Special thanks to Sian Townsend, Jessica Prince, Judi Coe, Perry Hastings, Kirsty Keegan, Kevin Lawrence (Abbeystar Print Solutions), Matt (The Earl of Beaconsfield), Judy Linford (The Art Department).

Cover photograph taken at Dixie's stall on the main Cambridge market. Find her there on Tuesdays, Thursdays, Fridays and Saturdays.

Five great reasons to shop indie

- around 60p of each £1 spent locally goes back into the local economy compared with a measley 5p if you spend it online or out-of-town

- it feels good: you can talk to local people who often have a great deal of expertise about what you are about to spend your hard-earned cash on

- fresher food, better service and greater choice of products

- the more indies we have, the more character our city has – who wants to live in a clone town full of sheep who buy what the big chains tell them to?

- it feels right: when you shop indie you are more likely to be able to trace where stuff comes from and it also reduces your carbon footprint

SPECIAL OFFER

Shop and save money – only with this book

Why not take advantage of the generosity of some of Cambridge's lovely independents and whenever you see the special offer price tag on one of the feature spreads, use this book to receive a little extra something special when you visit.

Just make sure you have a copy of the book with you!

Contents

Welcome to Independent Cambridge

Once again, our travels around the city and beyond have uncovered a truly amazing and vibrant independent scene. From artists and artisan bakers, butchers and boutiques to wine merchants and wool shops – all using their creativity and innovation to offer us something very special.

And it's true what 'they' say: every little really does help. You can make a massive difference by choosing to shop independently. If every adult in Cambridge spent just £5 per week in its independent shops instead of online or with the big chains, it would be worth an extra £24 million per year to the city's economy. That's because local independent businesses are more likely to employ local people and collaborate with other local businesses, meaning more of the money stays within the community rather than flowing into the coffers of big corporations.

So, whether you are a resident of Cambridge or a visitor, we once again urge you – support our independent traders and events – and we hope this guide will help you to discover the best of our city and local area.

Anne Prince

Anne Prince
Editor

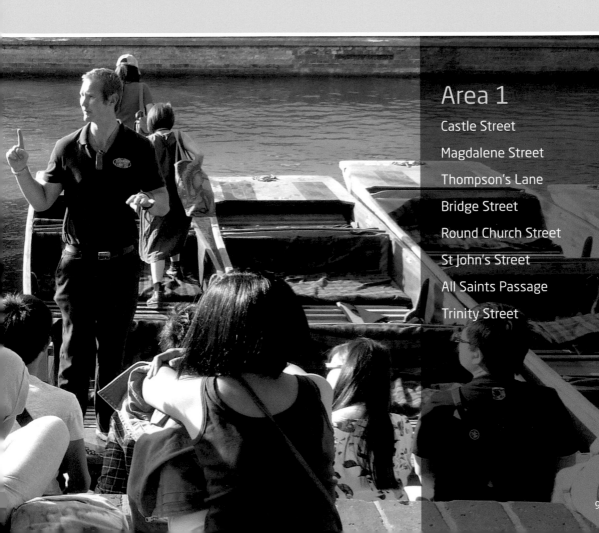

Area 1

Area 1

Castle Street, Magdalene Street, Thompson's Lane, Bridge Street, Round Church Street, St John's Street, All Saints Passage, Trinity Street

Castle Hill is where Cambridge began. The bronze sculpture at the junction of Magdalene Street and Chesterton Lane represents the layers of human habitation archaeologists discovered beneath it, with Roman remains, executed Saxons, and a lost medieval treasure – 1,805 silver pennies and nine gold coins that can be seen in the Fitzwilliam Museum.

'What are the brass studs in the pavement?' is the question most frequently asked by visitors.

The 600 brass studs in the Bridge Street and Magdalene Street pavements represent flowers that you can see carved on nearby college buildings – find the Marguerite above the entrance to St John's.

Allan Brigham

Museum of Cambridge (formerly Cambridge and County Folk Museum)

Just a short stroll from the river, past the many independent shops of Magdalene Street and aptly located in the most historic area of the city, is the fascinating and quirky Museum of Cambridge.

The Museum was founded in 1936 by leading members of the town and university with the aim 'to interest the ordinary citizen in aspects of local social life which were fast disappearing in Cambridgeshire' – an ethos which is still held today.

The Museum is housed in a wonderful 17th-century, timber-framed building which, for 300 years, operated as the White Horse Inn. The rooms of the inn have now been turned into 'settings', including a bar, a kitchen, the Fens and folklore room and a playroom and each room is packed full of intriguing objects alongside familiar household items – some dating back to the 1600s.

The permanent collection is continuingly being brought to life by the ever-creative temporary displays, events and family activities, some of which provide a genuine 'hands-on' approach to history by using original artefacts, documents and photographs.

The Museum is also home to a shop filled with unique and locally-made toys, gifts and games as well as cards and unusual books (great for presents) and a tearoom serving tea (eight flavours from Cambridgeshire-based Kandula Tea Company) and delicious home-made cakes (from local baker, Afternoon Tease), on pretty vintage crockery. All proceeds go to supporting the Museum.

Museum of Cambridge

2/3 Castle Street, Cambridge CB3 0AQ

Tel: +44 (0)1223 355159

Email: info@folkmuseum.org.uk

www.folkmuseum.org.uk

Tues – Sat: 10.30am-5pm

Sun: 2pm-5pm

Tearoom Sat: 10.30am-4.30pm

Walking along Magdalene Street, as the pavements begin to narrow and the buildings go back in time, there, nestled beneath the eaves of an important historical building is Bowns and Bis. The door opens into a large timber-framed space (once a 16th-century inn), with rails of gorgeous dresses, elegant work clothes and wedding outfits. The back of the shop leads you through next door to 'Bis' – another delightful space, with weekend, casual clothing and accessories.

The shop is the inspiration of Rosalind Bown: since studying fashion design, Rosalind has worked in most aspects of the trade from design and retail to bespoke tailoring. Bowns and Bis was established 15 years ago and, thanks to Rosalind's experience and brilliance in interpreting the next season's look, represents everything a shopper could wish for in the search for designer clothes.

Initially championing the 'Best of British' designers, the collection includes Paul Smith, Margaret Howell and Vivienne Westwood. In among these favourites, the selection has now broadened to include the most elegant designers from Paul and Joe and Carven to Schummacher and L'Agence – bringing the most exciting international labels together under one roof.

With Rosalind's professional advice at hand and friendly staff, any time spent shopping at Bowns and Bis is a joyous experience.

Bowns and Bis

24 & 25 Magdalene Street
Cambridge CB3 0AF
Tel: +44(0)1223 302000
Email: info@bownscambridge.com
www.bownscambridge.com
www.facebook.com/bownsfashioncambridge
Mon: 10.30am-3pm
Tues –Sat: 10.30am-5.30pm

Designer wear for every occasion

Della Kaur Owner: Della Gould

From its picturesque riverside setting in a beautiful medieval timbered building, Della Kaur brings the women of Cambridge gorgeous jewellery and accessories from designers and artists around the world.

Born in Africa, in an Indian family, trained in London as a jeweller and now living and running a business in Cambridge, it's not surprising that Della's influences are international as well as contemporary. From a successful on-line start, 2013 sees Della Kaur taking its place on the High Street with a stunning range of handcrafted fine jewellery from British and European designers alongside master jeweller

Christopher Powell who has practised for over 30 years in Cambridge as one of the UK's leading jewellery designers and makers.

For her pure pashminas, silk scarves and silk and leather bags, Della sources designs and material from India and Asia. She is passionate about taking ideas from different cultures and blending them with day-to-day fashions to work for contemporary women's lifestyles. Quality and provenance are hugely important to Della too and regular trips are made abroad to source materials and meet and talk with the artists, designers and craftspeople themselves to explore new possibilities and new products. This close working relationship also means that a number of products they make are limited one-offs or small run commissions that are customised individually to Della's own designs for a truly unique look.

Della Kaur

31 Magdalene Street
Cambridge CB3 0AF
Tel: +44 (0)1223 462256
Email: dk@dellakaur.co.uk
www.dellakaur.co.uk

Cambridge Wine Merchants (Bridge)

Cambridge Wine Merchants (CWM) was established in 1993 with the first shop opening up in Mill Road. CWM now has four lovely shops in the city – one still on Mill Road plus King's Parade, Cherry Hinton Road and the newly refurbished Bridge Street branch – known simply as 'Bridge'. Located just on the corner of picturesque Quayside, Bridge recently took over the shop next door to create a fantastic wine bar to take full advantage of the setting. Of course the other major advantage is that customers get to choose from the incredible range of over 600 quality wines – at shop prices! Buy by the glass or buy any bottle from the shop, pay a small corkage charge and sit and soak up the view. Simple platters of deli delights such as cheeses, olives and breads are included in the price. There's also a brand new whisky and spirit tasting bar with samples starting at just £1 from Bridge's carefully-chosen range of over 600 whiskies and 450 spirits.

The passion for all that they do is very obvious – just take a look at the website to see the huge number of accolades and awards the CWM team have received. 2013 alone has seen them win prestigious International Wine Challenge awards for Large Independent Merchant of the Year UK, Regional Merchant of the Year Eastern England and Fortified Specialist Merchant of the Year UK. So their mission statement – to be the best independent wine merchant in the county and to have fun doing it – sums up CWM perfectly.

Cambridge Wine Merchants
31/32 Bridge Street
Cambridge CB2 1UJ
Tel: +44 (0)1223 568989
Email: bridge@cambridgewine.com
www.cambridgewine.com
Mon – Thurs: 10am-9pm
Fri/Sat: 10am-10pm
Sun: 12noon-9pm

For great wines and happy times

free corkage with a copy of this book

SPECIAL OFFER

Heading off Bridge Street near the River Cam is Thompson's Lane – an unassuming little street in this historic part of Cambridge. Halfway down the lane and also unassuming, from the outside at least, is The Varsity Hotel & Spa.

The Hotel is the vision of a group of Cambridge University graduates and from the moment you step inside, it's obvious they intended to create something quite special in such an historical and beautiful location. Each of the 48 rooms are individually designed and named after Oxbridge Colleges, however if you are now thinking of a traditional, understated look then you would be wrong. Instead, think New York loft meets contemporary English style with incredible views of quintessential Cambridge, and you have The Varsity.

And the higher up you go, the better the views get, until you reach the simply stunning roof terrace with its panoramic view across the Colleges, River Cam and rooftops of Cambridge. Open to hotel and non-hotel guests alike, the terrace also transforms on some evenings into an open air cinema with large screen as part of the annual Cambridge Film Festival.

More beautiful views of the river can be found at the River Bar Steakhouse & Grill, located just next door and the menu looks pretty good too, with steaks that are dry-aged for a minimum of 28 days and a selection of fish freshly cooked on the grill.

To complete the experience is the Elemis spa, offering customised facials through to hot stone massages. There is also a wonderful jacuzzi overlooking the Cam with sauna and steam room on hand. A fully-equipped gym and studio with an array of classes are on-site too for the more energetic.

The Varsity Hotel & Spa
Thompson's Lane (off Bridge Street)
Cambridge CB5 8AQ
Tel: +44 (0)1223 306030
Email: info@thevarsityhotel.co.uk
www.thevarsityhotel.co.uk

Boutique chic meets classic Cambridge

Once again, this particular area of the city is home to a great little independent business – Café on the Round. Sited just opposite the famous Round Church (the origins of which date back to about 1130 AD making it one of the oldest buildings in Cambridge), the Café's building also has quite a history of its own. From florists to taxi office and from jewellers to clothes shop, the lovely old building has seen many commercial guises.

Now, under the ownership of Mal, Helen and Lara, Café on the Round happily serves locals and tourists alike with great, freshly-made coffee, baguettes, ciabatta, salads, cakes, pastries and more. Having previously run restaurants in Harrogate and York as well as having shares in a Mexican restaurant in Amsterdam, Mal has also added some interesting alternatives to the menu. Wraps, soft tacos or quesadilla come with various fillings and home-made refried beans and salsa. Everything is available as take-out, but if you have the time to stay, make your way upstairs where you can sit, have a break and enjoy a unique view of the Round Church and surrounding area.

All the team at Café on the Round are huge supporters of the local 'indie' scene and are always coming up with different deals to encourage the independent trade. For all their special offers, as well as the menu and details about ordering online – just visit the website or pop into the Café!

Café on the Round
16 Round Church Street, Cambridge CB5 8AD
Tel: +44 (0)1223 308279
Email: cafeontheround2@gmail.com
www.cafeontheround.co.uk
Mon – Fri: 7.30am-5.30pm
Sat: 8am-5.30pm
Sun: Sometimes closed

Great little café with great views

e, baguettes, teas, cakes

Free cup of coffee with this book

SPECIAL OFFER

Cafe on the Round

coffee, baguettes, teas, cakes

If you like your clothes to be design-led rather than necessarily label-led, and you appreciate a genuinely honest and personal approach to customer service, then you should pay Petrus on Bridge Street a visit.

The buying team of Petra, Steve and Faye, is passionate about the use of textures, colours, design and form as well as the comfort and fit of the clothes they choose. These passions are also reflected in the look and feel of the shop – funky retro-inspired lighting and minimalist fixtures are softened with classic original shop fittings and vintage pieces, all carefully designed and chosen to make visitors feel comfortable – something Petra and her team are particularly good at. In fact, sometimes customers have even bought some of the fixtures, so items in the shop are constantly changing.

A five year stay in Amsterdam for Petra and Steve before setting up Petrus (first in Saffron Walden and now the Cambridge shop), has definitely added a European flavour to their venture. Brands stocked include quirky Dutch brands Sandwich, whose clothes and accessories for women use unusual and high quality fabrics to create a distinct look, and G Star with a range for both men and women. New, unique and unusual mens- and womenswear are chosen to reflect stylish and contemporary ranges that fit perfectly with the Petrus ethos.

Petrus
67 Bridge Street, Cambridge CB2 1UR
Tel: +44 (0)1223 352588
www.facebook.com/petrusdesign
Mon – Sat: 10am-6pm
Sun: 11am-5pm

Spend £50 and get 10% off with this book

SPECIAL OFFER

If you are the type of person whose eye is caught by an interesting fabric design, a quirky accessory or a gift with a twist, then you really should make time to visit Lilac Rose clothes shop on Bridge Street.

With their creative flair, Mark and Amanda's vision was to bring a bit of theatre and fun to the High Street, with a central cast of beautiful British clothing from designers including Louche, Fever, Emily & Fin, Closet and Miss Patina. Brands are chosen in particular for their use of colour and fabrics, but most of all for their great fit and their slightly edgier take on the retro theme. The pricing is consciously 'High Street', but you don't need to worry about seeing the same dress being sported by the masses, as Mark and Amanda only stock a small number of each item and are constantly on the lookout to find new and interesting additions. This all adds to the sense of excitement and discovery at Lilac Rose and with a generous boudoir-styled changing room area and a very helpful and knowledgeable team, it's very easy to get caught up in the fun.

Supporting the central clothing range is an inspired collection of jewellery and accessories – from the utterly glamorous to the quirky and humorous. Lilac Rose is also a fantastic shop to find presents – from books and bags to cards and wrapping paper, all shot through with the shop's underlying eclectic theme.

Lilac Rose
71 Bridge Street
Cambridge CB2 1UR
Tel: +44 (0)1223 363330
www.facebook.com/lilacroseshop
Mon – Sat: 9.30am-6pm
Sun: 10am-5.30pm

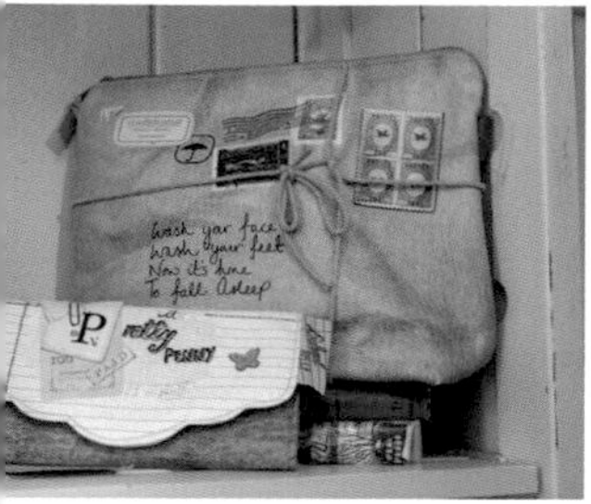

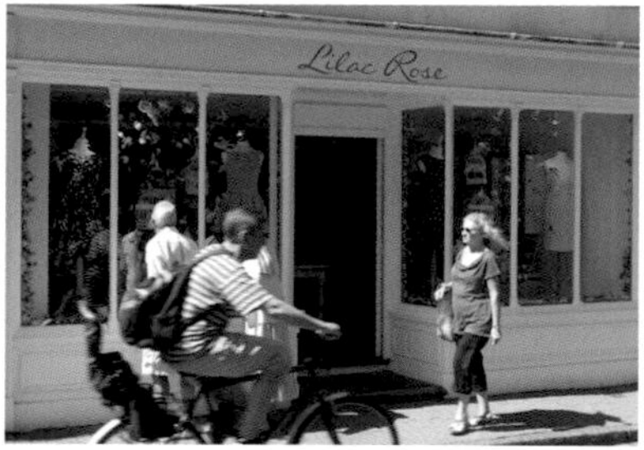
Lilac Rose

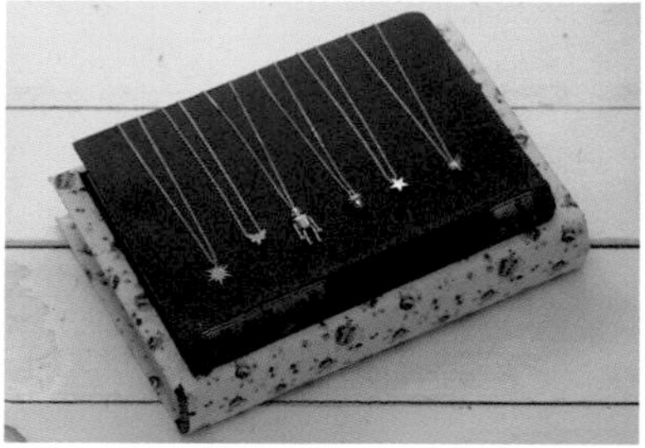

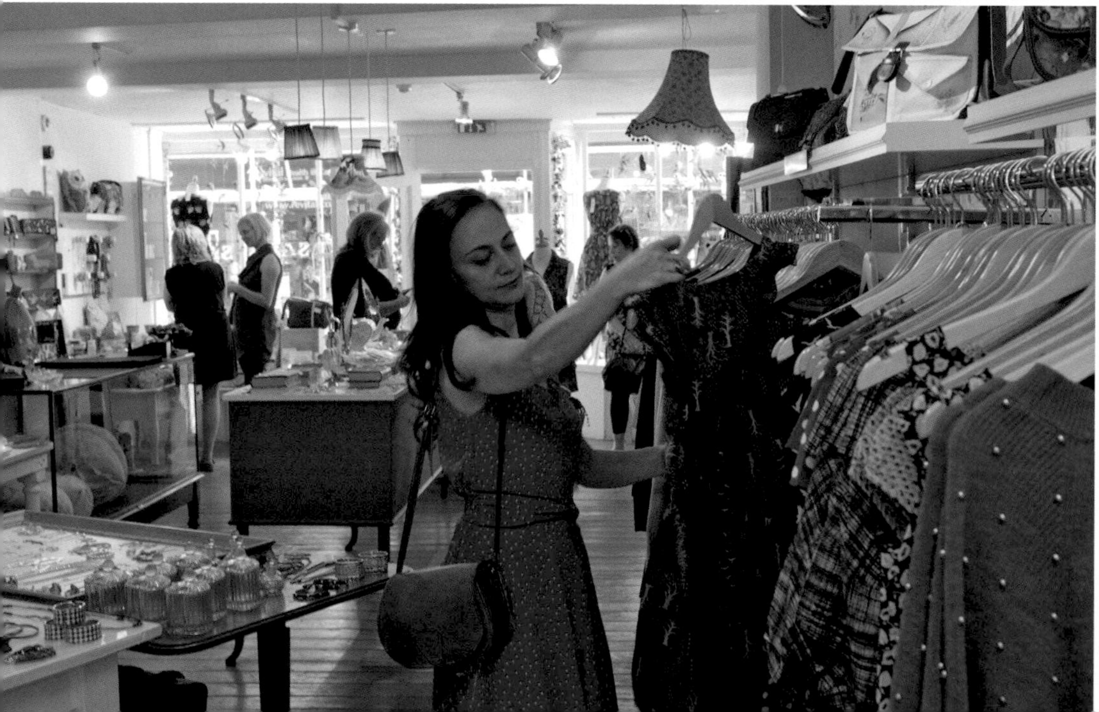

19:10 Owner: Alison

It could refer to a historical date or possibly be a nod to a birthday or anniversary. In fact Alison was sitting on the 19:10 London King's Cross to Cambridge train when she first discovered she had been given the go-ahead on her first ever business venture.

Although one of our youngest indies, Alison already had a wealth of retail experience and knew exactly which brands she was going to stock. Regular visits to Paris and Germany are part of her working life, as the European collections she chooses from are all about styles and designs that really fit with her customers' lifestyles. They are practical and comfortable but ooze design and individuality.

Danish brand Second Female has a streamlined, simple look whereas Two Danes and Masai are more fluid and bohemian. Rundholz Black Label from Germany and Xenia from Croatia are both incredibly wearable brands but with real edge and more than a touch of feistiness about them. Above all, the brands at 19:10 can be worn by women of any age and for any occasion – the same piece could be dressed-up for an evening out or worn in the day with leggings and sneakers.

The shop itself is designed with a similar ethos. Comfortable, natural colours and fittings are contrasted with an edgy industrial feel. The service too is helpful but unobtrusive and Alison and the rest of the 19:10 team love nothing more than watching customers try on new things and, most importantly, having fun!

19:10
72 Bridge Street
Cambridge CB2 1UR
Tel: +44 (0)1223 324468
Mon – Sat: 10am-5.30pm
Sun: 12am-5pm

Photographer: Adam Catling

"Have nothing in your homes that you do not know to be useful and believe to be beautiful." This quote by William Morris very neatly sums up all that you will find on a visit to Providence.

Located on the corner of Bridge Street and All Saints Passage, the shop with its lovely, large windows, contains two floors of beautiful, as well as practical, Colonial-influenced furniture and other finishing items for the home. Twenty years ago, Providence started out as cabinet-makers – producing pieces in oak and pine including freestanding kitchen dressers, larder cupboards and wardrobes. To finish the furniture in the Shaker style, Kathy and Tim developed their own Providence Paint and, as part of their original shop at Burwash Manor, were also one of the first places in Cambridge to stock paints from the Farrow and Ball range.

As well as the larger pieces of furniture, Providence also houses a selection of Shaker rails, shelves, cabinet hardware and traditional braided rugs. Complementing all this perfectly is an allsorts mixture of equally functional yet cleverly-designed home accessories – from brooms to baskets.

So, returning to the opening quote – why have an everyday potato masher when you can have one in the shape of a daisy from the sculptural Wildflower range by Bojje? Or why use a dreary duster when you can be cleaning the cobwebs away with one fashioned from ostrich feathers? As you can see, along with functionality, Providence combines stylish forms with a dash of vintage, a splash of colour and a great sense of fun.

Providence

73 Bridge Street, Cambridge CB2 1UR
Tel: +44 (0)1223 506556
www.providenceuk.com
Mon – Fri: 10.30am-5.30pm
Sat: 10am-5.30pm

Stylish forms with a dash of vintage

Prohibido Lingerie Owner: Mercedes Lee

Located in one of central Cambridge's historic passage ways, linking Bridge Street to St John's Street, is a small cluster of excellent independent shops including the beautiful and enticing Prohibido Lingerie.

Originally from Barcelona in Spain, Mercedes has brought a strong sense of European style and characteristic warmth to her boutique and with over ten years of experience in the lingerie business, her knowledge ensures she provides a stunning product range as well as an excellent lingerie fitting service to her customers. This expertise was rewarded when after only opening the door to Prohibido in 2010, in 2011 the shop won the Best Newcomer category in the national Stars: Underlines Best Shop Awards, which pays homage to the excellence of retailers throughout the UK and Ireland. Pretty good going in such a short space of time!

The contemporary brands stocked are from all over the world and cover the spectrum of fun fashion and everyday through to exclusive designer and classic elegance. Brands available include Stella McCartney, Pleasure State, Vivis Silk, Eberjey, La Perla and many others. Prohibido also has a great range of lovely swimwear, lounge wear and nightdresses.

Mercedes has also been meticulous when it comes to the boutique's design and layout – giving it a wonderfully intimate and luxurious 'boudoir' feel. Keeping her customers' comfort at the top of her list, a generous amount of the shop's space has been dedicated to the changing room area. Sumptuous curtains can be rearranged to suit one customer or up to 15 for the numerous 'lingerie parties' Mercedes and her team offers.

Prohibido Lingerie
5 All Saint's Passage
Cambridge CB2 3LS
Tel: +44 (0)1223 316553
www.prohibido.co.uk
Mon – Sat: 10am-6pm
Sunday seasonal opening

10% off with this book

SPECIAL OFFER

Anthony Owner: Tony Halls

Situated on historic Trinity Street, Anthony has served the discerning gentlemen of Cambridge for over 35 years. For that time, the owner, Tony Halls has focused on supplying the provincial customer with garments hand-picked from the best Bond Street collections.

Navigating current trends and sourcing only from the best manufacturers, Anthony creates a timeless aesthetic from contemporary shapes and colours. Tailoring from Canali, Pal Zileri and Tombolini forms the basis of the range, contrasted or co-ordinated with luxury accessories from all over Europe.

Swedish shirt makers Eton supply wrinkle-free, Swiss cotton shirts which prove ever-popular amongst Cambridge's business class.

For more formal occasions, Anthony hold ranges of black and white tie evening suits including an extensive range of bow ties. Weddings are well-catered for with morning dress, custom-made ties and waistcoats.

Made-to-measure and custom-made services are available in both tailoring and shirting which offer an exact fit and a personal touch. Appointments are available during the week until 8pm but must be arranged at least 24 hours in advance.

The experienced staff offer unhurried advice and the fitting and alterations are all part of the exemplary service.

Anthony
18 Trinity Street
Cambridge CB2 1TB
Tel: +44 (0)1223 360592
www.anthonymenswear.co.uk
Mon – Sat: 9am-5.15pm
Closed for lunch Mon – Fri: 1pm-1.30pm

18
Anthony
Trinity Street

CANALI

Jacks on Trinity Owner: Anne

A colourful new addition in 2013 to the city centre is the aptly-named Jacks on Trinity. Bathed in a sea of red, white and blue, Jacks is an unabashed celebration of 'Great Britishness' through its traditional and nostalgic iconography. The Union Jack adorns a huge range of items from T-shirts and sweatshirts through to bags, cushions, children's toys and of course the British classics of teacups, tea towels and teapots. This focus on tradition and heritage extends to the Royal Family too – fancy owning a solar-powered Queen and Corgi set? Or venturing downstairs you can have your photograph taken with the famous family in the form of life-sized cardboard cut-outs!

As well as being home to the other great London icons such as red post boxes, Big Ben and Beefeaters, Jacks has a high quality range of souvenirs featuring and celebrating Cambridge too. So, if you are a visitor to the city or a local who feels proud of living in such a beautiful place, Jacks is where you will find just the gift to show your love of all things Cambridge.

All the merchandise has been chosen for its quality (sometimes lacking in some souvenir shops). Button badges, postcards and stationery items are at the lower end of the price range with beautiful leather bags and fine china at the other. Anne has also picked up on the Great British sense of humour with products like saucy seaside playing cards and snow globes complete with cycling students against a backdrop of King's College Chapel – something every Cambridge home should have!

Jacks on Trinity

34 Trinity Street
Cambridge CB2 1TB
Tel: +44 (0)1223 354403
www.jacksontrinity.co.uk

15% off when you spend over £20

SPECIAL OFFER

It is very easy to feel just a little bit intimidated about stepping into an art gallery. You really want to go and have a closer look at what's on show, but may be put off by wondering if you will understand it or be able to afford to buy anything on display.

At cambridge contemporary art, in the beautiful and historic Trinity Street, you need not worry about such things. The staff are genuinely friendly and welcoming and more than happy to talk to you about the pieces on show and to tell you about the artists and craftspeople behind the work. Specialising in handmade prints, paintings, sculptures and crafts, the gallery first opened in 1990 and shows the work of over 100 UK-based artists, with a new exhibition every month.

Selected by the Crafts Council for the national list of craft shops and galleries, cambridge contemporary art also makes buying art easy as it's part of the nationwide *Own Art* scheme, which is designed to make it simple and affordable to buy original, high-quality contemporary art and craft. You can borrow up to £2,000, or as little as £100, which is paid back interest-free in equal instalments over a period of ten months. The gallery also offers gift vouchers and runs a wedding list service.

Towards the back of the gallery, it's also worth noting, is a fantastic selection of art greetings cards – on sale at a price below the amount asked by most High Street card shops. So, as you can see, there really is no reason to feel intimidated by stepping through the door.

cambridge contemporary art
6 Trinity Street, Cambridge CB2 1SU
Tel: +44 (0)1223 324222
Email: info@cambridgegallery.co.uk
www.cambridgegallery.co.uk
Mon – Sat: 9am-5.30pm
Sun and Bank Holidays: 11am-5pm

Cambridge University Press Bookshop

Having recently celebrated its 20th anniversary, the Cambridge University Press Bookshop is rightly situated in the very heart of historical Cambridge. From the site of number 1, Trinity Street, books have been sold since 1581, making it the oldest bookshop site in the country.

Uniquely, the shop sells books published only by Cambridge University Press; beautiful publications that cover the majority of non-fiction subjects. The ground floor presents new publications, a wonderful section containing local interest titles, shelves of the best-selling Companions series and cases full of books on the humanities and social sciences.

Venturing upstairs, a further wealth of knowledge is contained in the tomes on subjects including classics, law and mathematics, alongside business and management. Theology can also be discovered as well as Cambridge Bibles.

Three years ago saw the opening of the Learning Centre. This covers books for the younger generation with everything from children's books to GCSE and 'A' level revision. There is also a dedicated section for teachers and students of English and state-of-the-art computers where it is possible to try out different learning modules.

Cambridge University Press does not stop at books; with its digital printing, e-publishing and CD-Roms, the shop is a wonderful mix of history and modern values.

Cambridge University Press Bookshop

1 Trinity Street, Cambridge CB2 1SZ
Tel: +44 (0)1223 333333
Email: bookshop@cambridge.org
www.cambridge.org/uk/bookshop
Mon – Sat: 9am-5.30pm
Sun: 11am-5pm

Area 2

Area 2

Green Street, Sidney Street, Sussex Street, Hobson Street, King Street, St Andrew's Street, Victoria Street

Oliver Cromwell's head lies opposite Sainsbury's in Sidney Sussex College. Cromwell attended the college as a student, and was MP for Cambridge before becoming Lord Protector after the execution of Charles Ist.

Allan Brigham

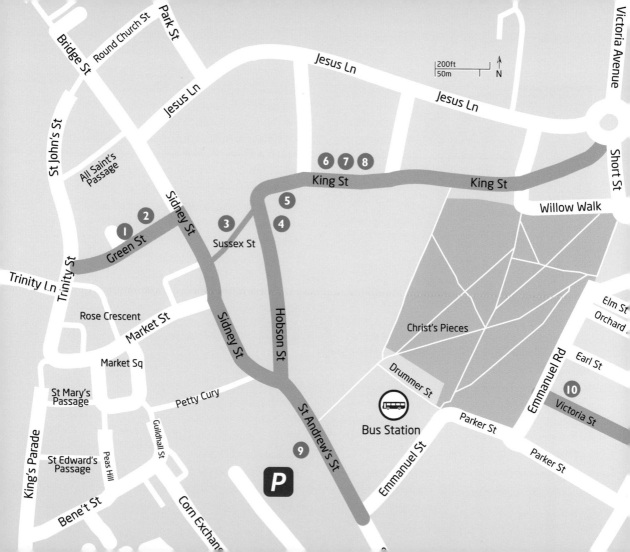

Opening the door to Open Air is the start of a whole new adventure. This boundless independent shop provides everything needed for all types of outdoor activities.

The shop was opened in 1990 by two individuals who combined their knowledge of the outdoor market and the use of equipment in extreme conditions to offer an alternative to the chain store ethic.

Refusing to be saddled with the narrow ranges normally offered, Open Air provides an extensive choice. Alongside European brands such as Bergans of Norway and Fjallraven, they support the British company Rab and many more.

Open Air is divided between three shops. Number 11 contains the splendid range of menswear and outdoor equipment. The adjoining number 12 displays the excellent range of women's clothing; the styles, colours and practicality have all been considered to great effect. A short walk down the road is number 15 where everything is provided for below the knee – from shoes and boots to gaiters and woolly socks.

The long-serving, knowledgeable staff are all active users of the products and are able to offer sound advice. The service they provide will ensure that you embark on your adventure with everything you need.

Open Air
11 Green Street
Cambridge CB2 3JU
Tel: +44 (0)1223 324666
Email: enquiries@openair.co.uk
www.openair.co.uk
Mon: 9.30am-5.30pm
Tues – Sat: 9am-5.30pm

For all your outdoor adventures

It would be hard not to be tempted by the window display alone, but step inside the door of 3 Green Street and it's instantly obvious why Modish has been recommended by The Guardian as one of the top 100 shoe shops in the UK.

Once you browse the shelves you will discover an incredible range of shoes to suit most budgets but without compromising style or quality. Sarah Decent, the owner of Modish, used to live in Rome and work in Madrid and this is reflected in the number of Italian and Spanish shoes that she stocks, often from little-known designers that are hard to get hold of in the UK. So whilst popular brands such as Fly London, Geox, Ruby + Ed, and Calvin Klein are always firm favourites, there's also something a little bit different from what's offered by the usual High Street chains.

But Modish isn't just about great looking footwear. Because fortunately for the women of Cambridge, Sarah's feet are a sample size 4 – which means she personally tries on everything she buys for the shop. If it's not comfortable, it doesn't make it onto the shelves at Modish, no matter how gorgeous it is.

And Modish was recently voted Cambridge's best independent shop in the 'Clothing and Accessories' category in local MP Julian Huppert's laudable 2013 initiative Discovering Cambridge – celebrating the city's best independent businesses. It's quite an achievement considering Modish has only been in Cambridge for two years!

Modish
3 Green Street, Cambridge CB2 3JU
Tel: +44 (0)1223 354436
Email: enquiries@modishonline.co.uk
www.modishonline.co.uk
Mon – Sat 9.30am-5.30pm
Sun: 11am-5pm

No pain, no gain? Not at Modish!

Spend over £30 on shoes and get a free necklace worth £15 with this book

SPECIAL OFFER

Established nine years ago, The Cambridge Toy Shop is the only independent toy shop in the city. It is a truly fabulous shop offering a brilliant selection of toys for all ages and within a broad price range – from pocket money and party present prices to gifts for very special occasions.

Vivienne makes regular trips to trade fairs in London and Birmingham to ensure the shop has all the most up-to-date toys and games. For younger children there is so much to see; little kitchens and shops, trains and cars – all there to fuel the imagination and help create their own worlds.

Moving through the shop there is more to discover – traditional toys such as the beautiful, handmade Merrythought English bears sit alongside ever-popular Sylvanian Families and Papo historical figures.

Downstairs, Lego and Playmobil favourites are in constant supply, and there is an amazing array of jigsaw puzzles, board games and modelling kits. Everything from Cambridge Monopoly and Bananagrams, to Corgi cars and Think Fun puzzles, there is always something to find and do. A recent addition has been a beautiful range of gift cards and gift wrap costing only £1.75.

To ensure everyone gets the most out of their visit, there is a great team of young people working at the shop (as well as real mums!) – ready with useful advice and always willing to demonstrate any of the toys. A loyalty card and deliveries by cycle courier are also available and weekends often see face-painting and displays, making sure that every visit is a fun-filled one.

The Cambridge Toy Shop
15/16 Sussex Street, Cambridge CB1 1PA
Tel: +44 (0)1223 309010
www.cambridgetoyshop.co.uk
Mon – Sat: 9.30am-5.30pm
Sun: 11am-5pm

THE CAMBRIDGE **TOY SHOP**

Lots More Downstairs

SPECIAL OFFER

10% off with this book

This local café takes its name from the Australian term 'to stickybeak,' which means to have a bit of a nosey. Owners Catherine Bolton and Lucy Robinson set up the café in 2010 and right from the start they knew they wanted the kitchen to be an integral part of everything so that people could have a 'stickybeak' at what was going on. And true to its name, head along and you can see your food being made and ogle all the gorgeous creations hot from the oven.

The café menu changes through the week, with everything from healthy salads and wholesome hot dishes for lunch, to indulgent cakes and puddings. The girls keep things interesting by bringing new flavours and combinations to the menu, influenced by their various travels. Along with their cheerful team, they make everything by hand in the on-show kitchen and they source key ingredients from trusted local suppliers. Plus they have a license to serve alcohol with food so you can even relax with a glass of wine over lunch.

Sundays at Stickybeaks are a bit different – they serve up an all-day brunch with all sorts of tempting options and they are proving very popular indeed. They also put on a range of supper-clubs through the year with local experts coming in to show off their skills. And you can even hire the café for private events and parties.

Never again be tempted by a chain in Cambridge city centre – head to Stickybeaks for lunch, brunch or just a big slice of cake.

Stickybeaks

42 Hobson Street
Cambridge CB1 1NL
Tel: +44 (0)1223 359397
Email: info@stickybeakscafe.co.uk
www.stickybeakscafe.co.uk

A great place to eat and meet

Spend over £10 and get a free regular sized hot drink

SPECIAL OFFER

Valid Mon - Fri only, with this book

stickybeaks

Boudoir Femme Owner: Pippa Sandison

Independent fashion boutique, Boudoir Femme, described by the Telegraph as 'The boutique for every Cambridge woman's little black book', combines carefully chosen original vintage pieces with desirable designer brands, jewellery, accessories and perfume.

Originally specialising in selling high-quality vintage evening wear, Pippa opened her new womenswear boutique in King Street in 2006, where over the past seven years Boudoir Femme has become widely recognised for its great range of labels, bringing together 'Everything a girl could want' under one roof.

Clothing brands in store include American Vintage, By Malene Birger, MiH Jeans, Selected Femme and Maison Scotch with shoes and accessories from Sam Edelman, Chie Mihara, Rebecca Minkoff and Lily & Lionel. Beautiful jewellery from Danish designers Jane Konig, Pernille Corydon, Catho and Hultquist complete the look.

Boudoir Femme's strong brand mix and excellent customer service have been recognised both locally and nationally with industry awards including Winner of Love Cambridge Best Customer Service Awards (2010), Finalist in the Drapers Womenswear Retailer of the Year Awards (2011) and a listing as 23rd in Drapers & Pure Top 100 inspiring independents in the UK (2013).

Pippa and her team regularly hold in-store events including art exhibitions, fashion shows and fundraising activities for local charities. Pippa has also made it possible for customers to shop Boudoir Femme online at the website address below.

Boudoir Femme
2 King Street, Cambridge CB1 1LN
Tel: +44 (0)1223 323000
www.boudoirfemme.co.uk
Mon, Tues, Weds, Fri, Sat: 10am-5.30pm
Thurs: 10.30am-5.30pm
Sun: Seasonal opening (see website)

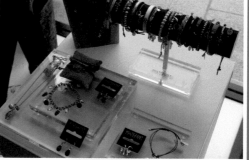

Local food lovers may have already heard of cake doyenne Afternoon Tease, also known as local baker Jo Kruczynska. Over the last year Jo has been baking cakes for local cafes including Hot Numbers and The Folk Museum and also running monthly supper clubs with co-host Ivana Gresham. But now Jo has opened her very own café in King Street and finally realised her lifelong dream. For the last seven years, she planned and saved up to open Afternoon Tease Café in Cambridge and in October 2013, all her hard work paid off.

Jo's inspiration to open her own place came from her round-the-world adventures and in particular the buzzing café scene she discovered in Australia, where coffee is akin to a religion. She'll be selling home-made cakes, fabulous proper coffee, breakfasts, light lunches and Jo's favourite meal of all – brunch. In fact, fellow brunch lovers will be able to indulge in their meal of choice all weekend.

Jo is determined that her cafe won't be your average 9 to 5 café; there will be events, pop-ups, live music and collaborations with other local foodies so you can expect the unexpected. Couple that with a laid-back, feel-good vibe and the friendliest service around and this café will become your new foodie favourite in no time.

Afternoon Tease Café
13 King Street, Cambridge CB1 1LH
www.afternoontease.co.uk

tempura prawns and soft-shell crab, to accompany authentic rice dishes, wok-fried or soup noodles, with a wide range of vegetarian options.

Freshly-squeezed juices and a good selection of wines and beers, including hot sake and oriental lagers, are available to compliment the food. There are also lunchtime specials, providing a satisfying meal at a very good price.

Everything is cooked to order and served straight from the open kitchen at the rear of the restaurant, with all stocks and sauces prepared in-house daily. The staff are friendly and always ready to accommodate any dietary requirements or even just to help choose!

Yippee Noodle Bar
7-9 King Street
Cambridge CB1 1LH
Tel: +44 (0)1223 518111
www.yippeenoodlebar.co.uk
Mon – Fri: 12noon-3pm and 5pm-10.30pm
Sat – Sun: 12noon-10.30pm

This unique independent noodle bar, of thirteen years, has consistently focused on combining fresh ingredients to create simple yet nutritious and flavoursome dishes.

The bright, contemporary interior is the ideal setting for this casual oriental dining experience. The menu offers many delicious appetisers such as spicy squid,

An authenic Oriental dining experience

Tindalls Arts and Graphics

As the largest independent fine art and graphics material shop outside of London, Tindalls on King Street is bursting with an incredible range of creative supplies – for the serious artist through to keen craftspeople, students and children.

Tindalls is a third generation, family-run business with a total of four branches in East Anglia. The first shop opened in Newmarket in the 1860s and in 2005, the Cambridge shop was purchased from Blackwells, which as most long-term Cambridge residents will know, was originally another family-run business – Heffers. Even today, some of the current staff once worked for this great Cambridge institution.

And along with the massive range of art and craft supplies, it's the staff at Tindalls who make the place so unique. Their collective knowledge of all things creative is immense and most of them have degrees in different art-related subjects, so there probably isn't a question they couldn't answer or a piece of artistic advice they couldn't give.

Stepping in to the shop, you can find a huge selection of paints – watercolour, oil, acrylic and gouache as well as paints for fabric, glass, ceramics, spray-paint, and even face-paint. Alongside easels, canvases, brushes, pens, pastels, pencils, sketch books, a huge range of different types of papers and boards are hundreds of different craft and modelling products and a section for children's activities too. Architectural students are also well-catered for with a range of specialist materials and technical drawing equipment.

Don't forget, if you can't find what you are looking for or need some advice – just ask!

Tindalls Arts and Graphics

15-21 King Street
Cambridge CB1 1LH
Tel: +44 (0)1223 568495
www.tindalls.co.uk
www.facebook.com/tindalls.gifts
Mon – Sat: 9am-5.30pm
Sun: 11am-4pm (Sept to Dec only)

For all things creative

WELCOME TO TINDALLS!

MOLESKINE
Legendary notebooks

Clamp Optometrists

Stylish, contemporary and with a thread of true passion running through all they do, the team behind Clamp Optometrists may be bang on trend with their unique designer eyewear collection, but they are also continuing a long tradition of independent opticians at their Georgian, city centre premises.

Opticians Hyman & Sons first operated from the site in 1908 and after various changes in ownership, Clamp Optometrists opened their doors in 2002. The current team consist of five optometrists, three dispensing opticians, five receptionists and one trainee optometrist. From eye care to eyewear, every member of the small team contributes to its eclectic

pool of talent. Known for their specialism in eye care, including for glaucoma, dry eyes and community health, the practice is also defined by its personality and friendliness.

This personality is most obvious in Clamp's luxury eyewear ranges – the vast majority of which comes from niche design companies including Paul Smith, Leisure society, Mykita, Barton Perriera, Maui Jim, Moscot and Bevel. In most cases, Clamp are the only stockist in the Eastern region of the UK. They work with designers who are able to react more quickly to reflect current trends. Clamp have such a close relationship with most of them, that customer comments as well as those from the team, can be fed back to influence and to evolve the spectacle design.

Clamp Optometrists
7 St Andrews Street
Cambridge CB2 3AX
Tel: +44 (0)1223 350043
www.clampoptometrists.com
Mon – Sat: 9am-5.30pm
Sun: 11.am-5.pm

From eyecare to stylish eyewear

Nestled in between Christ's Pieces and Parker's Piece is Duke House, a bed and breakfast so stylish that you'll be green with envy of anyone you recommend it to. Everything about this boutique haven is elegant, traditional and ever so charming. There are four double bedrooms, each named after a Duke and tastefully decorated. There is also a sitting room for guests, with comfy armchairs to recline into after a hard day's sightseeing.

Liz and Rob Cameron opened their super-stylish retreat back in 2012 when they saw a gap in the market for boutique accommodation, and it has been going strong ever since. The house itself dates back to 1840 and once housed the Duke of Gloucester so it really is fit for royalty.

Guests can enjoy a home-cooked breakfast in the dining room, complete with its own internal courtyard. The ingredients Liz uses are a local who's who; with bread from Cobs Bakery, bacon and sausages from Clarks of Ware, smoked salmon from River Farm Smokery in Bottisham, jam from My Dream Preserves in Histon and apple juice from Watergull Orchards in Wisbech. Plus guests are treated to something sweet from local cake lady Afternoon Tease in their rooms.

So next time you have friends, family or colleagues visiting, point them in the direction of this stylish retreat right in the centre of town. Duke House is a two-minute walk from the shopping centres and historic city centre so it really is the perfect base for exploring Cambridge.

Duke House
1 Victoria Street
Cambridge CB1 1JP
Tel: +44 (0)1223 314773
Email: info@dukehousecambridge.co.uk
www.dukehousecambridge.co.uk

Luxury boutique B&B

Area 3

Area 3

Market Passage, Rose Crescent, Market Hill, King's Parade, St Mary's Passage, St Edward's Passage, Bene't Street, Peas Hill, Trumpington Street.

The historic Market Square was the centre of commerce and of public life. Until the 1950s this was still the scene of Town and Gown riots every November 5th, a reflection of tensions in the town. As late as 1954 it was reported that home-made bombs were being tossed by the opposing sides and extra police had to be brought in from the county. The November 5th fireworks were moved to Midsummer Common to defuse the situation and today are a much-loved family event and the largest annual gathering of residents in the city.

The Corpus Clock, on the corner of Bene't Street and King's Parade, is a reminder not to waste time. It features a scary 'chronophage' who eats the hours. Costing £1million, it was a gift from engineer and inventor John Taylor who said: "I view time as not on our side. He'll eat up every minute of your life and as soon as one is gone he's salivating for the next". Taylor made his fortune from inventing the mechanism that turns off electric kettles once the water has boiled.

The best view in Cambridge is from the top of Great St Mary's tower. Do try it! The tower marks the starting point in 1725 of the first milestones in the country since Roman times.

Allan Brigham

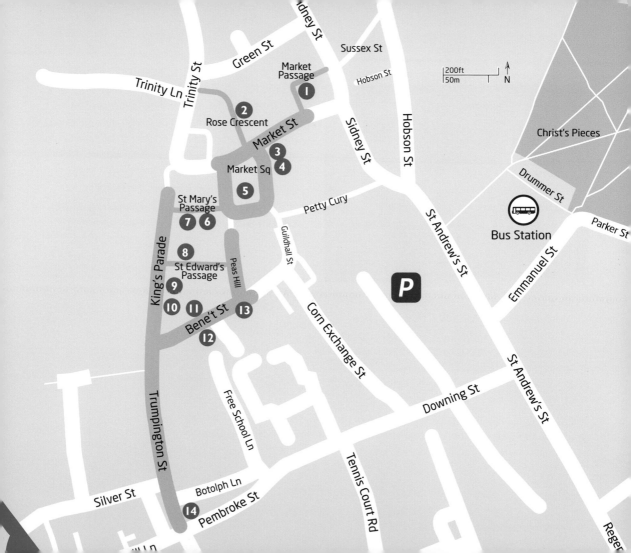

Ta Bouche

Nestled in amongst the city's most vibrant area is Ta Bouche, sister bar to the fabulous La Raza. The wonderful outdoor seating area on Market Passage gives the bar a marvellous continental feel. Aimed at a younger crowd, Ta Bouche has a unique character and its versatility is outstanding. Whether for brunch, lunch, dinner or drinks, this is the perfect location.

The welcoming ambience is relaxing – the décor is contemporary with walls enriched with black and white photographs. As the day progresses, so does the flow of music. Complemented by the swift service, the volume increases to more energy and fun.

Transcending into nightfall, you can continue with the extensive menu of modern European cuisine. Alongside this are marvellous cocktails – created by the talented bartenders – which can be spontaneous and conjured up to personal specifications. The cocktails are always popular and delight the young people, and all contribute to a good time.

This popular venue has everything you could wish for; its magnetic vibe will entice you back.

Ta Bouche
10-15 Market Passage
Cambridge CB2 3PF
Tel: +44 (0)1223 462277
www.tabouche.co.uk
Mon – Thurs: 10am-1am
Fri – Sat: 10am-2am
Sun: 10am-4pm, 9pm-12pm

La Raza

If anyone knows how to celebrate in style, it's the team at La Raza. And this is exactly what they have been doing, as 2013 has seen the 10th anniversary year for this popular bar. La Raza exudes all that is fabulous – food, drink and entertainment all encompassed under one roof. Recently refurbished and set in the middle of beautiful Rose Crescent, La Raza brings fun and sophistication to the very heart of the city.

Opening every day at noon, the bar slowly transforms throughout the day. Starting with lunch, there is a delicious Mediterranean menu of tapas and salads, fish dishes and paellas. Complemented by a glass of wine from the well-sourced list, what better way to spend a relaxed, comfortable time. Barista coffees are served all day which creates a smooth transition into the evening. The bar is open for aperitifs and a delicious range of award-winning, hand-crafted cocktails (they even have their very own gin blend called LaRaza01), followed by dinner – food to share, hot and cold dishes and a great selection for vegetarians. Then, at 9pm, the bar goes through its final transition of the day as the music begins to play.

La Raza is known as a great place for dancing. There are live bands every week with regulars such as Booga's Electric Sauce and Swagger guaranteed to get the crowd swinging. Wednesday nights are acoustic nights and, running alongside DJ events, jazz evenings and The Early Night club, there is always an event for everyone at this versatile venue.

La Raza

4-6 Rose Crescent, Cambridge CB2 3LL
Tel: +44 (0)1223 464550
www.laraza.co.uk
Mon – Thurs: 11am-4pm, 7pm-1am
Fri – Sat: 11am-4pm, 7pm-2am
Sun: 11am-3pm

Here's to the next 10 years!

Don Pasquale Owner: Pasquale Benedetto and family

Picture the scene – you are on holiday and stumble across a bustling market square full of fruit and vegetables, flowers and flavoursome food items. On the corner of the market you notice an inviting terrace – full of tables and green umbrellas and people enjoying a morning coffee or a delicious-looking lunch. This image of the Mediterranean is kindly bought to you and the centre of Cambridge by the independent Italian restaurant Don Pasquale.

Established in 1973, Don Pasquale has been run by the same family ever since and enjoys a reputation for classic Italian cuisine, well-prepared and simply presented. With its Pizzeria and Gelateria, lovers of all things Italian can feel perfectly at home and children are well-catered for too with their own menu or half portions of all the main pasta dishes.

As well as breakfast, brunch and lunch, the atmospheric restaurant is also open in the evenings for dinner. The seven-page menu offers pizzas, pasta, antipasto, salads, ciabattas and home-made desserts and if you need a recommendation, we suggest the Spaghetti alla Carbonara, the Penne con Pollo or one of the amazing Calzone Pizzas followed by the Affogato all' Amaretto. There is also a great selection of wines and Italian coffee.

Completing the authentic sense of a classic Italian restaurant is the open kitchen where you can watch a member of the family at work – always a positive sight in any restaurant.

Don Pasquale
12A Market Hill, Cambridge CB2 3NJ
Tel: +44 (0)1223 367063
Email: info@donpasquale.co.uk
www.donpasquale.co.uk
Mon – Sun: 8am-11pm

Subtly-signed off the busy central market square, 12a Club is a private members' club offering friendly, knowledgeable, attentive service in very elegant and relaxed surroundings.

The whole ambience is that of the prohibition era speakeasy – you feel transported from the real world outside into a relaxed but exclusive setting (just think Gatsby!). The main lounge and bar area has been opulently decorated 20s style and large leather booths beckon you invitingly. The bar itself is immense and the cellar incredibly well-stocked. Brilliant bartenders are happy to add a 12a twist to a traditional cocktail, serve you a classic glass of champagne or quench your thirst with a perfectly chilled beer.

Staircases lead off the main bar to the Red Room (small and intimate and perfect for an important meeting or a quiet drink with old friends) and the Purple Room (larger and fully-equipped with audio visual kits for presentations, training sessions or workshops). With the added bonus of wi-fi, daily papers and great coffee, the Club is a very special 'office away from the office.'

It's not all about work though. Its central location makes it a great place to rest during a major (indie) shopping-spree, with food to keep you fully-charged in the form of the best cheeses and charcuterie, antipasti and nibbles and hand-prepared canapés. 12a Club is also a sought-after venue for events from wine tastings to jazz evenings and cocktail workshops to fashion shows.

12a Club
12a Market Hill
Cambridge CB2 3NJ
Tel: +44 (0)1223 350106
Email: info@12aclub.com
www.12aclub.com

Opposite the Guildhall is Cambridge's Market Square where around 100 stall holders set up each day to provide both visitors and locals with a colourful choice of goods and services.

Traditional market products such as fresh fruit, vegetables and flowers mix with Artisan bread, olives, health foods, fish, books, crafts, clothes, jewellery, antiques, records and CDs and retro homewares and is ever-changing as new stalls arrive. There are a number of stalls offering services too – it's possible to have your clothes mended, get you bicycle fixed and get a haircut, all without leaving the Market Square. There's also a growing choice of 'street food' – much tastier than a sandwich from one of the nearby chain stores.

On Sundays (and bank holiday Mondays), the offering at the market changes when the stall holders for the Arts, Crafts and Local Produce Market lay out their wares. Introduced about 9 years ago, this market offers a quality selection of produce and products from the regions artists, craftspeople, photographers and farmers including unique T-shirts, gifts, jewellery, pottery, sculptures and organic foodstuff. It's also possible to pick up customised items as some of the stall holders can create these to your own design – so an opportunity to shop both independently as well as creatively.

General and Sunday Markets

Market Square, Cambridge CB2
Tel: +44 (0)1223 457000
Email: citycentremanagement@cambridge.gov.uk
www.cambridge.gov.uk/markets
General Market, Mon – Sat: 10am-4pm
Sunday Market, Sun: 10am-4pm
(and bank holiday Mons)

Walking into some boutiques can be an intimidating experience – stern assistants, eye-watering price tags and overly clinical surroundings can halt you on the doorstep – but you need have no such fears at Cuckoo.

The genuinely bright and cheerful welcome from Michelle, Kate and the other members of the Cuckoo team is reflected in the layout of the shop too. White wooden floorboards and the use of reclaimed Victorian doors for the fittings gives a comforting, no-fuss feel, while showing off the range of clothes, accessories and gifts perfectly.

Originally inspired by the eclectic mix of items available in the markets and streets of Islington, Michelle and Kate have succeeded in bringing a fun,

London-style shopping experience to Cambridge. Always conscious of textiles, textures, patterns, cut and the real 'wearability' of clothing, Cuckoo chooses the designers it stocks on these criteria. Marilyn Moore, Odd Molly and Bombshell are amongst other lovingly-picked ranges, which collectively mix quirky designs with practical items to wear every day.

Complementing the clothes are gorgeous accessories including handbags, an ever-changing collection of jewellery, beautiful scarves and girly gifts that are sure to please as presents for others or just for you.

The Cuckoo team are also on-hand to share their inspiration and expertise through their new style and colour guidance service – whether on a one-to-one basis or as an evening session for a group of friends (with a glass of fizz!), you couldn't wish for a more relaxed and fun way of shopping!

Cuckoo

4 St Mary's Passage, Cambridge CB2 3PQ
Tel: +44 (0)1223 364345
Email: info@cuckooclothing.co.uk
www.cuckooclothing.co.uk
Mon – Sat: 9.30am-6.00pm
Sun: 11.00am-5.00pm

For a truly original look

It is difficult to walk past Ark without being enticed in by the fabulous window display and then, the door opens onto an emporium of delightful treasures. This unique shop has the most eclectic selection of items where gifts can be found for interesting people.

Regular trips are made across Britain and Europe to source the best items – show-stopping crystal creature jewellery, a massive spectrum of coloured leather Italian bags, and fabulous lamps that illuminate childhood memories. Longstanding relationships with British companies see a constant supply of favourite items; wonderful leather gardening gloves from Shropshire and soothing, scented, paint-tin candles from Cumbria. There is also a great section dedicated to the very young; traditional and modern toys with a classic twist.

Always initiating new concepts, Jane has put in place an easy-to-use online ordering system. It offers free next-day delivery, or if you live in Cambridge, Ark can usually deliver the same day by cycle courier and even gift-wrap your purchase if desired. What a service – especially if you've just realised you've forgotten an important birthday!

Jane's aim for Ark has always been to sell things that nobody else does – and that has certainly been achieved. From school bells, scorpions in paper weights, to chocolate lightbulbs, beetles in marbles and phrenology heads – there is always something intriguing to be found and something new waiting to be discovered.

Ark

2 St Mary's Passage, Cambridge CB2 3PQ
Tel: +44 (0)1223 363372
www.arkcambridge.co.uk
Mon – Sat: 9.30am-6pm
Sun: 10am-5pm

In 1896 the original G David (a Parisian bookseller) started selling his books from a stall in the central market square in Cambridge. Today, if you take a short walk from the market towards the Cambridge Arts Theatre and King's College, just next to St Edward's Church, you will find G David Bookseller in St Edward's Passage which surrounds the Church and has remained largely unchanged for centuries.

There could hardly be a more perfect location for a traditional bookshop specialising in antiquarian books, fine bindings, second-hand books and publisher's remainders, so step inside G David Bookseller – fondly known by its customers simply as 'David's'.

Owned and run by the most welcoming team you could wish to meet, David's has that sense of being from another time – almost as if you have arrived at a location for a film where an archetypal English bookshop is required as a setting by the director.

Wind your way through the heavily-stocked rooms at the front of the shop and this 'film-set' sense is heightened when you walk into the antiquarian book room. Specialising particularly in English literature, early science and travel, the room contains about 4,000 beautifully bound books that surround you on shelves, in bookcases and on a large central table.

Hours could be spent here quite easily.

G David Bookseller
16 St Edward's Passage, Cambridge CB2 3PJ
Tel: +44 (0)1223 354619
Email: g.david.books@gmail.com
www.gdavidbookseller.co.uk
Mon – Sat: 9am-5pm

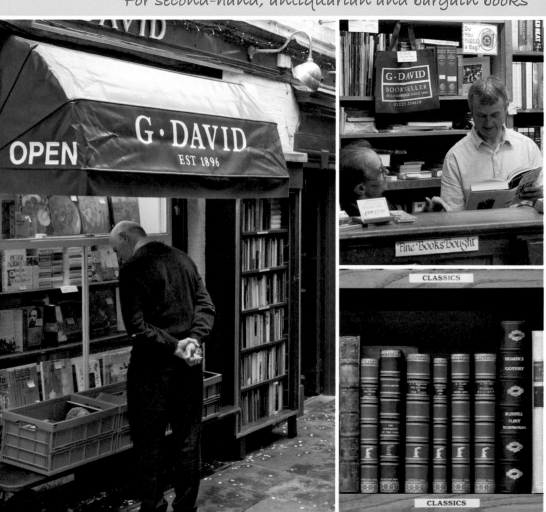

Primavera's main gallery, with views directly into the entrance of King's College and through to the Backs, is located on King's Parade in a beautiful listed building on three floors, the first of which was once the home to the essayist and poet Charles Lamb.

Step inside, experience and enjoy Primavera's unparalleled collection of contemporary handmade jewellery, ceramics, glass and silverware, scarves and ties, pewter, sculptures, glorious paintings, furniture, wood and jewellery boxes. Contact Sophie Thwaites regarding wedding lists and special commissions.

Primavera supports Cambridge Open Studios and represents many Cambridgeshire makers. Your purchase supports not only independent Cambridge, but over 400 talented artists and designers. Appointments can also be made to see other fine displays of furniture, paintings, ceramics and glass at Primavera's smaller gallery on Magdalene Street CB3 0AF, at 6 Wellington Court CB1 1HZ, and College Farm in Haddenham CB6 3XD. First Edition Translations, Primavera's sister company, is based at 34a Fitzroy Street CB1 1EW.

Primavera
10 King's Parade
Cambridge, CB2 1SJ
Tel: +44(0)1223 357708
Email: contactprimavera@aol.com
www.primaveragallery.co.uk

Nomads Owner: Fin Hague

Seeing photographs of his grandfather on a mapping expedition to Tibet, a young Fin knew instantly that travel was in his blood too. Initially travelling to Afghanistan as a teenager and falling in love with the culture he found there, the question was, how could he fund further journeys? The answer – to find and buy beautiful items and bring them back to Cambridge to sell, and so the seeds for Nomads were sown.

Fin continues to satisfy his wanderlust with annual trips, now mainly to India and Nepal, to discover new aspects of the cultures as well as sourcing interesting ranges for the shop. In fact all who work at Nomads love travel, which probably explains the friendly openness and enthusiasm of everyone there.

To discover for yourself what Fin has collected along the way, all you need to do is take a short walk downstairs at Nomads. The shop, which has now been in business for over 25 years, is on two floors but the lower floor really is a true Aladdin's cave. Afghan rugs, scarves, shawls and stoles, clothing, throws, lampshades, wooden boxes, Tibetan singing bowls, tribal artifacts, stationery and musical instruments fill the room. And the range of jewellery is particularly impressive, the majority of it coming from Jaipur – the hub of the jewellery industry in Rajasthan.

Nomads also transforms into an atmospheric venue for evening talks and concerts – information for which can be found on the Nomads Facebook page along with stories and music from around the world.

Nomads

5 Kings Parade, Cambridge CB2 1SJ
Tel: +44 (0)1223 324588
Email: nomadfin@gmail.com
www.nomads.uk.com
Mon – Sat: 10am-6.30pm
Sun: 12am-5pm

SPECIAL OFFER

10% off when you spend over £20 with this book

Sister gallery to cambridge contemporary art in Trinity Street, cambridge contemporary crafts was opened in 2009 to showcase the ever-expanding range of crafts.

Housed in a beautiful 16th-century building located just opposite St Bene't's Church, the oldest church in the city, and two doors down from the famous Eagle pub (where Francis Crick announced that he and James Watson had discovered the structure of DNA), the gallery is another attraction making this historic street a worthwhile destination for locals and visitors alike.

Showcasing crafts handmade in the UK, cambridge contemporary crafts holds a huge range of work by up and coming as well as established craftspeople in the mediums of ceramics, glass, textiles, wood and jewellery. Throughout the year, the ever-changing display promotes the work of these artists and craftspeople – look out for, amongst others, the wonderfully glazed ceramics by local artist Katharina Klug, delicate porcelain bowls by Mizuyo Yamashita, sculptural jewellery by Zelda Wong and stunning, bold jewellery by Tatty Devine.

As in the Trinity Street gallery, the atmosphere is friendly and genuinely helpful and prices start from just a few pounds. The Art Council's Own Art scheme is also available, making it easy and affordable to buy original, high-quality contemporary art and craft. You can borrow up to £2,000, or as little as £100, which is paid back interest-free in equal instalments over a period of ten months. The gallery also offers gift vouchers and runs a wedding list service.

cambridge contemporary crafts
5 Bene't Street, Cambridge CB2 3QN
Tel: +44 (0)1223 361200
Email: info@cambridgecrafts.co.uk
www.cambridgecrafts.co.uk
Mon – Sat: 10am-5.30pm
Sun and Bank Holidays: 11am-5pm

More
beautiful
handmade work
Downstairs

Andrey Pronin took over this quirky little gift shop in 2012 after graduating from Fitzwilliam College. The Russian-born entrepreneur decided to rename the shop Podarok, which is Russian for 'gift' and inject an element of fun and funkiness to all they do.

Podarok now stocks an eclectic mix of everything from jewellery to lampshades, leather satchels to pocket money toys – so there really is a gift for absolutely everyone and every budget. Plus, it's always nice to know that Andrey goes to great lengths to ensure his stock is ethically sourced. For example Podarok stock Fikay bags, a Fairtrade company who recycle concrete bags into gorgeous bags, wallets and accessories and then gives a portion of each sale to providing an education for children in South East Asia. The shop is also very supportive of British artists. Cardinky and Dynamo prints, Heather Stowell jewellery from Ely, mugs from Stoke-on-Trent and they frequently have artists and craftspeople approach the store to display their designs.

There's also exquisite jewellery from Michael Michaud – an American designer who produces items cast from real flowers and leaves and decorates them with precious stones, plus beautiful soft leather satchels from Vida Vida and unique, colourful lampshades from Lush of Greenwich.

The other rather special thing about this gift shop is the wonderful window displays that change every week, themes have included 'under the sea', 'fairy woodland' and 'on the beach'. At Podarok you can find a gift for anyone and everyone, perhaps even a nice little something for yourself!

Podarok
12 Bene't Street
Cambridge CB2 3PT
Tel: +44 (0)1223 314411
Email: info@podarok.co.uk
www.podarok.co.uk

Pint Shop Owners: Richard Holmes and Benny Peverelli

As Independent Cambridge goes to press, Pint Shop is in the process of being built, but come early November 2013 this brand new, central independent will open its doors.

The focus will be on great meat, bread and beer, with a good glug of gin thrown in for good measure. Diners can expect a weekly-changing menu with a heavy slant towards great meat. The restaurant will use three core cooking principles; spit-roasting, charcoal-grilling and slow-cooking and you can expect one from each on every menu. As well as hearty meat, there will be lighter market fish and vegetarian options on offer.

The beautiful four-storey building on Peas Hill that they will call home will house a traditional bar area with snacks and light lunch options and a more formal dining room. On the bar you will find 16 taps of British craft beers, a selection of whiskeys and 40 gins, including a specially distilled pea gin from Cambridge Distillery – to pay homage to their new home. Plus of course, a small wine list for those who prefer a glass to a pint.

This exciting new independent will also serve a bargain pre-theatre menu consisting of two courses for £10 and three for £12.50 – to cater for those off to one of the two neighbouring theatres. And if you fancy a nibble post show then evening grazing menus will also be available for late night snacking over a drink.

Pint Shop
10 Peas Hill, Cambridge CB2 3PN
www.pintshop.co.uk
Twitter: @PintShop

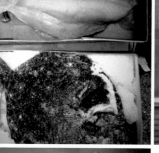

In 2011, Cambridge University alumnus Stephen Fry posted on Twitter that his favourite tea shop and bakery – Fitzbillies, was closing. Living in London at the time, but born and raised in Cambridge, Alison read the tweet and the idea to save a Cambridge institution was born.

So in August 2011 (after a lot of hard work), the 90 year-old story of Fitzbillies started a new chapter. The Grade II listed Art Nouveau frontage has been restored and the interior has a new and fresh look. Its famous Chelsea buns, baked using the original recipe, are as outrageously sticky as they have always been; trying one has to be on your 'list of things to do in Cambridge'. In addition to the buns and other tempting cakes and pastries, Fitzbillies has a lunch menu – including savoury tarts and pies (from the bakery), soups, salads and sandwiches – which changes daily to reflect seasonal availability.

Another new Fitzbillies storyline has been the addition of an exciting new dinner menu – currently available on Thursday, Friday and Saturday nights. The menu changes weekly (it's uploaded on the website usually on a Tuesday), and to give an idea of the style of food, dishes have included starters of baked figs with White Lady cheese, walnut and honey and Fitzbillies mutton ham, spiced apricots, potted mutton on toasted potato rosemary bread. Main course offerings have seen delicious combinations such as aubergine charlotte, dandelion, croutons and mustard dressing and also braised rabbit with cos, bacon and new potatoes. And of course the desserts are pretty good too – well they would be!

Fitzbillies

51-52 Trumpington Street
Cambridge, CB2 1RG
Tel: +44 (0)1223 352500
Email: manager@fitzbillies.com
www.fitzbillies.com

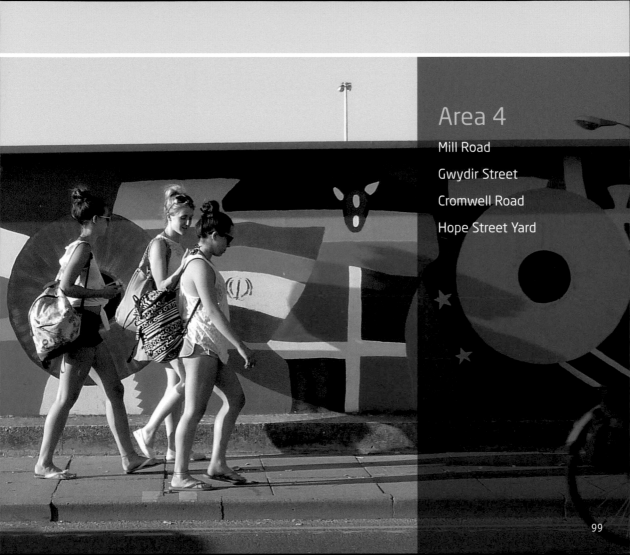

Area 4

Mill Road

Gwydir Street

Cromwell Road

Hope Street Yard

Area 4

Mill Road, Gwydir Sreet, Cromwell Road, Hope Street Yard

Mill Road used to be called Hinton Way (the way to Cherry Hinton). The road still ends in a footpath that leads to Cherry Hinton. Today's name comes from the windmill that stood near the Salvation Army shop (hence Mill Street too). The shop was previously Fine Fare, Cambridge's first supermarket! Before that it was The Playhouse cinema.

Romsey Town was known as 'Little Russia' after the Master of a Cambridge College referred to the striking railwaymen who lived there as 'Bolsheviks' during the General Strike in 1926.

Allan Brigham

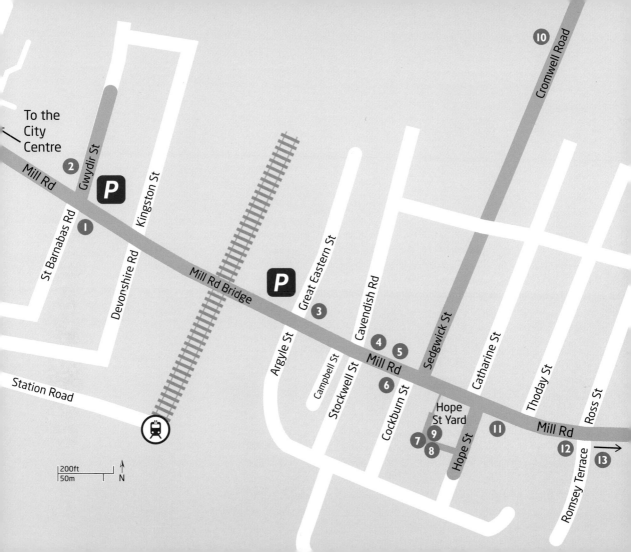

It's hard to believe looking around the stylish and modern interior at Taank Optometrists that an optician's practice has actually existed at 92A Mill Road for exactly 100 years, with Henry Flanders originally opening a combined chemist, dentist and opticians at the site in 1913. Today, owner Anjana Taank, believes in combining some of those traditional values of customer service (provided by her and her very experienced staff) and community involvement with the most up-to-date eye health technology and eyewear fit for the seriously fashion-conscious.

With her experience, of working as an independent optician as well as in the hospital eye service and voluntarily abroad, Anjana is certainly someone you feel is passionate about what she does as well as incredibly knowledgeable in her chosen field. She continues to work closely with Cambridge's Addenbrooke's Hospital – in the Glaucoma Clinic within the Eye Department and the practice also provides clinical services for the hospital. This professional work has involved investing in the latest equipment as well as specialised training, so there is no doubt you are in safe, expert hands with Anjana. And if you are (literally) on the lookout for top quality, fashionable frames and sunglasses, Anjana's range is hand-picked and selected to reflect style as well as quality. Both British and international designers are chosen for their unique, cutting-edge approach to design and production, with the range including Lanvin, Booth and Bruce, Markus T, the award-winning William Morris London, Maui Jim, Porsche and the stunning range of hand-crafted buffalo horn frames from Hoffmann.

Taank Optometrists
92A Mill Road
Cambridge CB1 2BD
Tel: +44 (0)1223 350071
Email: info@taankoptometrists.co.uk
www.taankoptometrists.co.uk
Mon – Sat: 9am-5.30pm

SPECIAL OFFER

Half-price eye exam with this book

1913
ONE
HUNDRED
YEARS
2013

Taank Optometrists

Photographer: Adam Catling

Fondly named after a record shop in the neighbouring street, often frequented by Simon as a youth, Hot Numbers coffee house is testament to what you can do if you have passion. In Simon's case – passion for music, machinery and most of all, coffee.

After studying mechanical engineering, it was music that took saxophone-playing Simon to Australia where the world of great coffee houses was waiting. After learning the trade, he returned to the UK, firstly to fix coffee equipment for indies in London, then back home to Cambridge to open his very own coffee house.

We may be getting spoilt for choice as to where to get our High Street coffee fix, but there is one important factor that sets Hot Numbers apart – its own roastery. Using single-origin, high-quality Arabica beans (sourced by direct trade) small batches are roasted to a medium degree to retain distinct flavours that can be lost in darker roasts. Carefully controlling the roasting techniques, ensures Simon gets the best taste depending on the origin of the beans as well as the season.

Hot Numbers roasts two to three different origins of coffee and these change seasonally so there's always something new to try (and new for Simon to experiment with!). From espresso-based to filter, you can have your coffee drip-brewed or syphon-style under the halogen lamp to truly appreciate the subtleties a great cup of coffee can present!

There is a great range of Sri-Lankan teas as well as breakfasts, lunches and delicious cakes – all using ingredients and produce sourced from local suppliers. A recent collaboration with the art gallery next door has added another dimension (literally) and with live gigs on Thursday nights – we return nicely back to Simon's original love – his music.

Hot Numbers
Unit 6, Dales Brewery
Gwydir Street
Cambridge CB1 2LJ
Tel: +44 (0)1223 359966
Email: info@hotnumberscoffee.co.uk
www.hotnumberscoffee.co.uk

October 2012 saw the new-look Earl of Beaconsfield open its doors when Susie made the change from being a pub regular to being its new licensee.

As well as looking for a new challenge, Susie had always been on the lookout for a pub that served lovely wine as well as lovely real ales – and that was a place where female pub-goers could feel comfortable. Add to this a wide range of lagers and ciders, great whiskies, music and food, and the pub's philosophy starts to become very obvious.

The refurbishment of the Beaconsfield sees a new, welcoming interior, with neutral colours and the nice table-top addition of flowers and candles, a planted courtyard area and a separate pool room off the garden. Susie has also installed an Italian pizza oven to be able to serve hungry customers a range of stone-baked pizzas.

For wines and whiskies, Susie works with another local independent – Cambridge Wine Merchants – whose experts help to select the tempting range. Add an ever-changing choice of superb Cask Marque real ales, a selection of refreshing draught lagers, two draught ciders and a growing number of American and European craft lagers and the result is a pretty impressive bar!

So, to the music! A packed weekly calendar sees acoustic and blues jams, Irish folk sessions, and guest acts playing everything from traditional jazz standards through to gypsy swing.

The Beaconsfield has it all – including the most lovable pub dog ever – Smoky Bacon!

The Earl of Beaconsfield

133 Mill Road, Cambridge, CB1 3AA
Tel: +44 (0)1223 410703
Email: hello@earlofbeaconsfield.co.uk
www.earlofbeaconsfield.co.uk
facebook.com/TheEarlofBeaconsfield
Twitter: @EofBeaconsfield
Sun – Wed: 12pm-12am
Thurs – Sat: 12pm-1am

A thriving community pub

Urban Larder has been on The Broadway in Mill Road for nearly three years, having outgrown its original home in Hope Street Yard. Its fast-gaining popularity for good, locally-sourced food is not surprising with delights such as local honey, jams from the Country Markets, meats, cheeses from The Wobbly Bottom Farm, healthy ready-meals, Saffron Ice Creams, pickles, mustards, local farm eggs (duck and hen) and 100 percent organic bread – kneaded by local people, with heart and soul in every loaf!

Alongside all the yummy food, is a growing display of work by local artists, lovely wrapping paper, cards and gifts. Polly is currently forging new relationships with some great up-cycling/recycling companies making both original and exciting work and Urban

Larder's online shop gives access to larger interior pieces for the home and garden (commissions often undertaken).

Polly has also gained a reputation for stocking some of the widest range of gluten and wheat-free food as well as a variety of vegetarian treats. A very popular addition to the lunchtime menu is the superb Greek slice. Made from 'his mother's own recipe', Yannis (from Crete) brings Polly fresh Spanakopita – a spinach and goat's cheese feta slice in olive oil pastry.

With its pretty and quirky seating area and with a calendar of fun evening events and its general place as a 'hub' for many of the locals, the Urban Larder provides the community with so much more than just its great selection of sustainable food and gifts!

Urban Larder

9, The Broadway, Mill Road
Cambridge, CB1 3NA
Tel: +44 (0)1223 212462
Email: info@urbanlarder.co.uk
www.urbanlarder.co.uk
Mon: 12pm-5pm
Tues – Sat: 10am-6pm
Sun: 11am-5pm

10% off
eat-in
lunch bill
with this
book

**SPECIAL
OFFER**

Urban Larder *eat local*

Fish is prepared – deep-fried, grilled or pan-fried – all cooked to order. You can also have your batter gluten-free. Alongside traditional fish such as cod, haddock and plaice, the regular menu carries delicious alternatives including fish stew, calamari, salmon, trout, bream, sea bass and fisherman's pie. Other seasonal treats on offer include grilled Cornish sardines, scallops and Shetland mussels, and just to add that little extra uniqueness, to accompany your fish is a range of home-made sauces.

As if that's not enough choice, you can visit The Sea Tree for Sunday Brunch (April – Oct) from 11am till 2pm where grilled kippers, Eggs Benedict, kedgeree and Eggs Florentine are amongst the featured dishes.

Mill Road's alternative fish bar, (finalist in the BBC Radio 4 2011 Food and Farming Awards and Highly Commended in the Best Newcomer category at the UK National Fish & Chip Awards), certainly offers the fish lovers out there a large number of alternative ways to get their fish fix. A traditional takeaway fish and chip shop The Sea Tree has a number of stylishly simple wooden tables for dining in-house, and a wet fish section.

Fresh fish deliveries arrive from Grimsby or direct from Billingsgate Market. David also insists that their suppliers provide written guarantees that the fish is from traceable and sustainable well-managed sources.

The Sea Tree

13/14, The Broadway, Mill Road
Cambridge, CB1 3AH
Tel: +44 (0)1223 414349
www.theseatree.co.uk
Mon: 5-10pm
Tues, Wed, Thurs: 12-2pm, 5-10pm
Fri: 12 noon-2.30pm, 5-10pm
Sat: 12 noon-10pm
Sun: 10am-2pm (April – October), 5pm-9pm

The Sea Tree

Bamboo Hairdressing Owner: Eddie Rose

Mill Road is home to many great independent businesses and passionate independent owners. One of these is Bamboo Hairdressing, owned by Eddie Rose whose career in hairdressing started over 19 years ago. Alongside Eddie at the unisex salon are Andy, Rosa, Jade and Ying – all experienced stylists and also long-term friends. Looking at reviews on the web confirms how the team's skills, ability to listen to their customers combine with that all-important relaxing atmosphere, to make it a sort-after salon throughout Cambridge as well as further afield.

One particular aspect Eddie was keen to bring to Bamboo was a very organic approach to the products the team uses. The Organic and Mineral Research Institute range is the chosen colouring system which uses natural ingredients as an alternative to traditional chemical-based colouring products – particularly good if you have any skin allergy problems. Eddie has clients travelling to him from London for these very popular products. Part of this range is the Seaweed Lightener – which unlike chemical bleach, contains no ammonia and is nourishing and conditioning at the same time. Daniel Fields Watercolours are also used to provide long-lasting colour but with no peroxide or ammonia content.

As well as traditional hairdressing services, Bamboo offer special styling for weddings, balls and other special occasions, hair extensions, massage and beauty treatments, free fringe trims and a generous student discount. This generosity also extends to the local community as they regularly partake in charity events and you can always see the team enjoying themselves on the day of the Mill Road Winter Fair!

Bamboo Hairdressing
202 Mill Road
Cambridge CB1 3NF
Tel: +44 (0)1223 502930
www.bamboohairdressing.co.uk

20% off for new clients with this book

SPECIAL OFFER

Just off main Mill Road is Hope Street Yard – a community in its own right, with a fantastic mix of independent traders – including the very unique and very colourful School Run Centre, also known as Cambridge Dutch Bikes.

The popularity of this European style of bike is evident throughout the streets of Cambridge. You will be hard-pressed to find a teenage girl (in particular), who is not pedaling around on a Dutch bike – with the ubiquitous wicker basket on the front. Also proving incredibly popular as well as practical amongst young families, are the wonderful child-carrying bikes and tricycles stocked by Hugh in his School Run Centre. The different permutations on how to transport varying numbers of small children as well as the weekly shopping (and your pet dog) appear endless but all catered for. And as the Yard is traffic-free, you can test drive a Cargobike, mummybike, tandem or tricycle easily and in safety.

As well as being kitted out for your 'wheels', you can satisfy your accessory cravings too. Baskets, matching panniers and child seats are all available to complete the look.

All of the bikes are imported directly from Holland, with brands including Azor, Bakfiets.nl Cargobike, Bakfiets.nl Cargotrike, BSP and Onderwater.

The School Run Centre
Hope Street Yard, Mill Road, Cambridge, CB1 3NA
Tel: +44 (0)7772 738899
www.schoolruncentre.co.uk
Weds – Sat 12-6pm

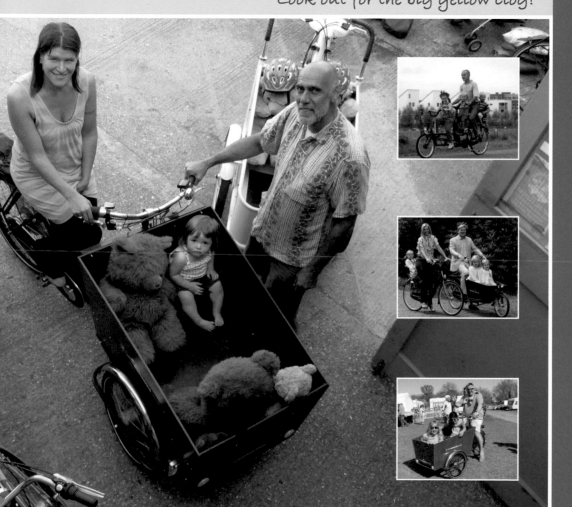

Makers' Gallery Owner: Neil Christie

Hope Street Yard comes up trumps again on the indie front, as just upstairs from Hugh's amazing collection of Dutch bikes, is home to the Makers' Gallery where Neil has transformed the space into a gallery as well as framing studio.

Having worked at Rowan for 12 years – making sculptures from wood, stone, metal and clay, Neil felt his creative ambitions were better-realised through setting up his own business. A self-taught artist, who for many years has run painting and drawing classes at various places including Cambridge's Fitzwilliam Museum, Neil sees being independent work-wise a creative thing too.

At the core of his venture is the bespoke framing service. Using his artistic eye as well as his practical skills, Neil produces all the framing work himself from an extensive selection of mounts and mouldings. As you can imagine, with his many years of working with a wide range of materials, help and advice is always on offer however creative or unusual the framing request.

Adjacent to the framing studio is the gallery space where Neil has the opportunity to exhibit his own paintings, drawings and sculptures. This 'artspace' is also home to life-drawing classes taught by Neil – giving him the chance to share his life-long passion for art. The classes are for those over 16 and his aim is to give newcomers to life-drawing a friendly introduction, while providing more experienced artists with the chance to develop their study at their own pace.

Makers' Gallery

3-4 Hope Street Yard
Cambridge CB1 3NA
Tel: +44 (0)1223 414870
Email: neil@makersgallery.co.uk
www.makersgallery.co.uk
Tues – Fri: 11am-7pm
Sat: 10am-5pm
Sun – Mon: Closed

Fantasia popped up in Hope Street Yard during summer 2013, but the upstart is already a casual crossroads for Mill Road residents, artists and enthusiasts of the eccentric. It mixes quirky original pieces, (notably 1950s Japanese mementos and kimonos), with French and English vintage fashion, toys, games, and artwork by neighbourhood friends.

A slapdash museum of unusual 'yukata' fabric is hung up to inspire students and other creative souls who brave Fantasia's inner recesses. Upcoming innovations might include 'technical' jewellery and wearable experiments in 3D printing. Brainstorming ideas for design, independent retail and the Mill Road community over a coffee, is always one of Fantasia's *raisons d'être*.

Romsey Retro's motto is 'finding forgotten treasures' and over time Clair has polished, repaired and painted old items so they can find new owners.

The original stories of these objects have been lost, but when they leave Romsey Retro they become part of a new story. A pair of 19th-century teacups became a wedding gift. A tall Art Deco lamp, newly rewired, now lights a Victorian house. An Ercol rocking chair found a new home in London. William Morris curtains decorate a Georgian house in Lincolnshire and a tiny Harris Tweed flat cap, found in Amsterdam, is now being worn by a local toddler.

Fantasia

Hope Street Yard, Mill Road, Cambridge, CB1 3NA
Tel: +44 (0)7921 004090
www.fantasia.uk.com
Twitter: @FantasiaMillRd

Open daily (except Mondays and Thursdays), from noon till 6 or 7pm.

Romsey Retro

Hope Street Yard, Mill Road, Cambridge CB1 3NA
Email: romseyretro@gmail.com
Twitter: @RomseyRetro
Weds – Sat: 11am-5pm

Just off Mill Road, on the Romsey side of the bridge and at the end of either Sedgwick Street or Catharine Street, is a relatively new addition to the growing contemporary and visual art scene in the city – the Cambridge Art Salon.

Celebrating its second birthday in September 2013, the Salon is an old motorbike shop turned makeshift arts centre for the community of Cambridge, offering work space and gallery space to members of the public. Working as an artist can be very isolating, but at the Salon there is the chance for people to meet, support each other and also collaborate in a nurturing and affordable environment.

And of course there is the opportunity to purchase creative work – what better way to support independent artists and designer-makers? Cambridge Art Salon has, on-site, a range of artists and creative practitioners working in contemporary arts and creative media, with a small shop that showcases some of their works. The gallery shows a vibrant range of artists from all backgrounds, many already established internationally or locally, wanting a relaxed environment to try out a new idea – or just starting out. Exhibitions are obviously regular events on the calendar and so are art classes for both adults and children.

The Cambridge Art Salon also pioneers contemporary arts projects with a community focus, such as 'The Cambridge Art Walks Map', which aims to make the city's broader art scene more accessible to the public. In 2013, they launched the first ever Romsey Art Festival.

Cambridge Art Salon

29 Cromwell Road, Cambridge CB1 3EB
Tel: +44 (0)1223 244391
Email: info@cambridgeartsalon.org.uk
www.cambridgeartsalon.org.uk
Thurs: 5.30pm-7pm Fri: 10am-5.30pm
Fri evenings: private views & opening parties
Sat – Sun: 10am-5.30pm

Photographer: Martin Bey

Photographer: Kevin Symonds

Sometimes translation from one language to another, particularly if it's a cultural reference, can be difficult. Liliana describes her shop as containing 'dreams'. This sounds strange until you hear the story of a customer for whom she made 900 large, white origami Japanese paper cranes for her wedding day. The customer had wanted white lanterns but Liliana explained these would traditionally have been exclusively used at funerals and not for weddings, so the birds were suggested and painstakingly hand-created instead.

This story sums up Dreams of Eastwind. Not only is it a place where you can find unique and often handmade items, but also a place where you can discover the real culture of the Orient and receive incredible service too.

Dreams of Eastwind started in 2001, selling antique pieces of furniture and other items imported from China as well as all over Asia. Now the shop stocks an incredible range of the most beautifully crafted and decorated Chinese boxes that come in all sizes, shapes and colours, pretty teapots, dolls, jade and other types of handmade jewellery, traditional games, calligraphy and painting sets and handmade cards. There is also has a fabulous and very interesting collection of old traditional musical instruments – from around the world and unique in Cambridge.

With some of the lovely gift items costing from as little as 50 pence, you just really need to walk over the bridge on Mill Road to see for yourself what Dreams of Eastwind will have in store for you.

Dreams of Eastwind

224 Mill Road

Cambridge CB1 3NS

Open 7 days a week

Situated on the Romsey side of Mill Road bridge, Cutlacks is not only the archetypal Aladdin's cave of all things for the home and garden but is also, thanks to Steve, very much at the heart of the local community. There wouldn't be a Romsey Garden Club if it wasn't for Steve!

Cutlacks has been trading (from its other shop in Ely) for over 160 years and that sense of traditional customer service and help from your local hardware store is still very much part of the current shopping experience. DIY advice is readily offered on the large range of products in that department as well as in all the others – kitchen, home and gardens, bedroom, bathroom and linen, cutlery glass & china and curtains.

Alongside traditional products for the home and garden you can find many contemporary ranges including Joseph Joseph, Denby, Fired Earth, Soda Stream and Mike's Homemade and AGA, Farrow and Ball and Little Greene available through the Ely store. You can also find an extensive range of jars and bottles and a fantastic home brewing section that all goes to make Cutlacks infinitely practical as well as a pleasure to the eyes of some of its more design-conscious clientele.

A constant stream of shoppers visit Cutlacks – by foot, by bike, by bus (there is a stop just near the shop) but for those planning to buy larger items, there is a car park or they can get their purchases delivered – all part of the service.

Cutlacks
264 / 268 Mill Road
Cambridge, CB1 3NF
Tel: +44 (0)1223 246418
www.cutlacks.co.uk
Mon – Fri: 9am-5.30pm
Sat: 8.30am-5pm

Looking to start any building project can be pretty daunting, particularly if it involves planning permissions and building control. With over 25 years of structural design, project management and construction experience, Matthew and his team calmly and comprehensively cover all aspects of both domestic and commercial projects – from initial site meetings through to completed construction.

With the increasing need for documentation and installation certificates, ever-changing regulations, official sign-offs and approvals, it's hard for the average lay-person to have the time, let alone the knowledge, to organise any sizable construction project. Although very happy to offer assistance with a single design or construction task, Matthew

is also trained in using AutoCAD (Computer Aided Design). So, for larger projects, he is able to produce full-colour drawings and if you require, incorporate structural engineering elements within these too.

Moving along the project timeline will probably bring you to the door of the local authority – to apply for planning permission and seek the all important approval of building control! Once again Matthew is able to liaise with the relevant people on your behalf, using his in-depth knowledge to get the go-ahead and approval needed.

So now it's time to start building – the final stage and one Matthew is more than able to manage. Training on the restoration of the monastic Priory and Cannonry surrounding Ely Cathedral through to complete development of modern housing, shows the breadth of skills and experience Matthew and the Timber-Tech team bring to any project.

Timber-Tech Construction Ltd
388 Mill Road, Cambridge CB1 3NN
Tel: +44 (0)7831 365929
Email: contact@matthewwilliams.biz
www.matthewwilliams.biz

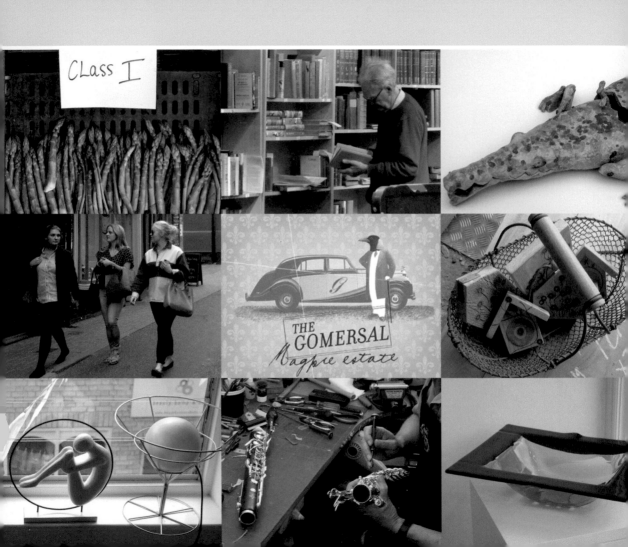

CLass I

THE
GOMERSAL
Magpie estate

More To
Discover

NEW SEASON BRITISH
RASPBERRIES £2·50
→ IN FRIDGE

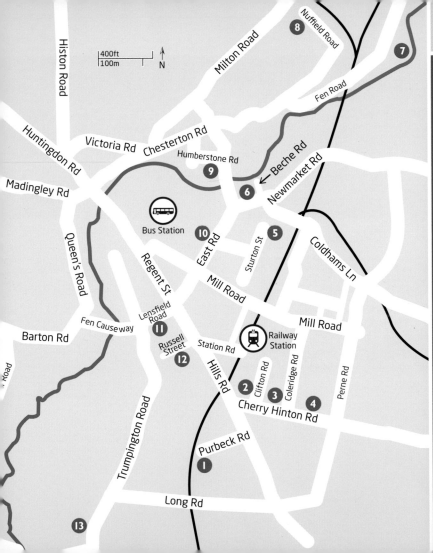

Outside the city

Whether you are looking to sharpen up your cookery skills or organise a unique event, Cambridge Cookery School is a fantastic local independent just off Hills Road that offers everything from lessons to private parties.

Head chef Tine Roche trained at the world-renowned Leiths School of Food and Wine and has been imparting her knowledge along with a team full of local experts since 2008. Tine's Scandinavian heritage means real bread is her personal passion, but classes range from bread baking to knife skills, children's classes to courses just for gents. There is something for every age and every skill level and they all take place in the state-of-the-art kitchen complete with Neff ovens and beautiful iittala cookware.

For an event with a difference the cookery school can also host everything from birthday parties to corporate entertaining. Tine and her team excel at running private events and can work with you to devise a bespoke itinerary and menu. You can choose to be waited on hand and foot restaurant-style, or have a go at cooking some of the food yourself.

This unique approach is also a fantastic way to lease your own private restaurant for the night – get a group of 10 or more of you together and you can have a bespoke menu, cooked for you by trained chefs and served up in the delightful kitchen.

Cambridge Cookery School
Unit 9D, The Imre Building
Homerton Business Centre
Purbeck Road
Cambridge, CB2 8HN
Tel: +44 (0)1223 247620
www.cambridgecookeryschool.com

For fresh ideas on food

Cambridge Cookery School

Free gift for all that bring this book in with them

SPECIAL OFFER

Cheffins Fine Art Auctioneers

The name of Cheffins has been synonymous with the fascinating world of auctioneering in the Cambridge area for a very long time – with archives of auctioneers' sales books dating back to 1825. Some Cambridge residents may also remember that on the current site, on the corner of Cherry Hinton Road and Hills Road, there actually stood a cattle market – once owned and run by Cheffins.

Today, Cheffins Fine Art Auctioneers occupies a modern building containing two sales rooms which hold regular sales throughout the year. These range from antiques and interiors and art and design from 1860 to specialist books, maps and prints, fine art and fine wines. You can find a calendar of when these sales are happening on their website which also contains a lot of really useful details about viewing and the sales themselves. Beautifully produced, full-colour catalogues are available containing hundreds of wonderful photographs of the items coming up for auction.

The main auction room itself is very atmospheric and, on the day of a sale, becomes almost theatrical! But if you can't physically get to a sale, Cheffins now offers online live bidding through its own website as well as other commercial auction sites.

If your interest is in selling, as one of the UK's leading auctioneers, Cheffins' specialists cover the whole of the country – advising on single pieces through to entire collections. Every Tuesday between 11am and 3pm their valuers are on-site and on-hand at the Cambridge sales rooms to offer free verbal valuations.

Cheffins Fine Art Auctioneers
Clifton House, Clifton Road, Cambridge CB1 7EA
Tel: +44 (0)1223 213343
Email: fine.art@cheffins.co.uk
www.cheffins.co.uk

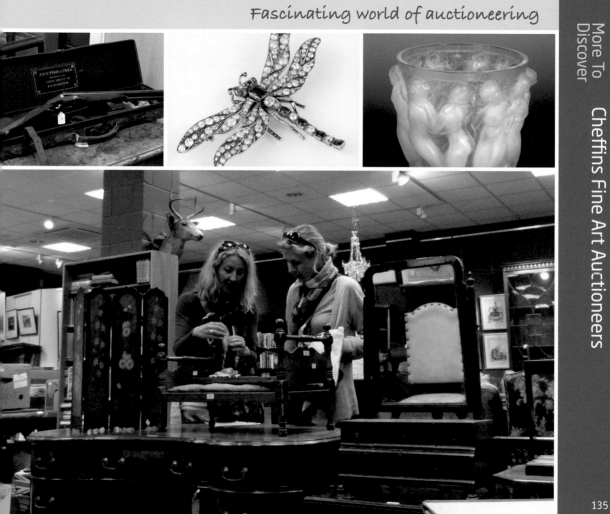

Cambridge Wine Merchants (Cherry)

It may be the newest of the four beautiful Cambridge Wine Merchants' (CWM) shops in the city, but there's been a wine shop on this same site for over 50 years.

'Cherry' as it is affectionately known, is probably the most 'locals-orientated' of the branches, with a strong focus on education too. As well as being a multi award-winning wine retailer, CWM are also a certified Wine and Spirit Education Trust (WSET) course provider – with courses running at Cherry.

At the back of the shop is a charming and cosy seating area which is used for wine tastings, the wine courses and as a venue. With seating for 45 inside plus tables outside, you can hire this lovely space for a particular celebration or simply buy a bottle of wine and sit and enjoy it. There's a menu – offering cured meats, cheeses, nuts, breads and dipping oils – all perfect to accompany the hundreds of different choices of great wines. Events are a regular occurrence with CWM combining forces with local independent foodies such as Inder's Kitchen, Steak & Honour and Jack's Gelato to bring a great food/wine combination to the people of Cambridge.

Prices of wines range from £4 to over £1000 and with close links to the makers and producers, the quality of all the products they stock is extremely high. A fine selection of premium artisan gin, vodka, aged rum as well as an impressive range of whisky all add up to make Cherry so much more than just your average local off license.

Cambridge Wine Merchants

163 Cherry Hinton Road
Cambridge CB1 7BX
Tel: +44 (0)1223 214548
Email: cherry@cambridgewine.com
www.cambridgewine.com
Mon – Thurs: 11am-8pm
Fri/Sat: 11am-10pm
Sun: 12noon-8pm

So much more than just a wine shop

free corkage with a copy of this book

SPECIAL OFFER

CAMBRIDGE WINE MERCHANTS

Importers Wholesalers and Retailers of Wine Beer and Spirits

More To Discover

Cambridge Wine Merchants (Cherry)

One of the youngest and newest of our featured independents, James has completed his first trading year and now has a group of happy customers to sing his praises.

Although at the beginning of the independent road, James is a fully-qualified, time-served bench joiner with a background in the construction and installation of doors, windows and staircases.

The new enterprise is all of the above plus customised, hand-crafted furnishings and fittings for domestic and commercial environments.

Offering a bespoke service, James will build and install elegant replacement sash windows to meet modern building regulations; craft doors from selected softwood or hardwood; design and fit a unique staircase or create a tailored piece of stylish fitted furniture to sit perfectly in the room it was made for. Mouldings, too, can be made to accommodate the different quirks, dimensions and angles of any room – particularly those of period properties and they can also be recreated to match existing moulding details.

From the initial choice of wood used, through to the different finishes available, James uses his experience and expertise to offer advice as to the best options depending on the job in-hand. He also understands the potential restrictions surrounding planning regulations and listed building status and so ensures all of his work is carefully designed, not only to the highest standards of craftsmanship but also to work perfectly and practically in-situ.

Linford Joinery
217B Cherry Hinton Road
Cambridge CB1 7DA
Tel: +44 (0)7449 834098
Email: james@linfordjoinery.co.uk
www.linfordjoinery.co.uk
www.facebook.com/Linfordjoinerycambridge

Affordable bespoke joinery for your home

FLACK magazine

Published for the first time in October 2011, FLACK is a local 'what's on' magazine with a big difference. It covers the sort of events happening in Cambridge that can take a bit more effort to find out about – the ones that are not advertised with big promotional budgets but are popular with people in the know. Films and exhibitions to stand-up comedy and live theatre, music and even bike maintenance workshops – and most are free or at least very affordable.

The other big difference is FLACK Magazine is not only sold by homeless people, it's produced by them too. FLACK contains local Cambridge content and the 'what's on' listings, articles, artwork and recipes are all written by the core team members – homeless people themselves. By writing, editing, producing and distributing FLACK, members of the homeless community gain skills, support and a sense of vocation, at the same time as raising awareness of who they are and what they have to say. Anyone with experience of homelessness is welcome to participate in this process.

As well as the magazine, FLACK has a film unit which is available for commissions of film projects of all kinds and also offers awareness workshops for professionals who work with homeless people. You should also check out their beer can camera kits which you can buy from the website – the images they produce are amazing. So, as you can see, FLACK is definitely a whole lot more than just a magazine.

FLACK magazine
City Life House
Sturton Street
Cambridge CB1 2QF
Tel: +44 (0)1223 366532
Email: info@flackcambridge.org.uk
www.flackcambridge.org.uk

SPECIAL OFFER

10% off annual subscription with code IC2

The Sheep Shop Owner: Sarah Clark

Wanting to be surrounded all day by colour was not the only reason Sarah decided to open her own business in November of 2011. A keen knitter, she knew that Cambridge needed a shop selling premium wools as well as yarns from the local area. She also wanted to create a place that was friendly, touchy-feely and somewhere where customers could linger and chat over a cup of tea.

Sarah has succeeded in all of the above at The Sheep Shop, a finalist in the Cambridge Business Excellence Awards 2013. She stocks a colourful kaleidoscope of luxury yarns including cashmere, llama, alpaca and soft merino wools. A range of gorgeous hand-dyed sock yarns from Cambridge-based indie dyer Sparkleduck are particularly covetous, as are the elegant 'field to fashion' clothes and alpaca knitting kits from local company Purl Alpaca Designs.

It's not just high-end yarns at The Sheep Shop though. Sarah has searched for budget yarns too, that are also lovely and soft and fun to knit. There's a great selection of needles, felting materials, crochet hooks, ribbons, buttons, books, patterns – pretty much all you need to get creative.

Don't worry if you're not a knitter yet – you can join one of the many knitting and crocheting classes that take place at the shop and start learning and on The Sheep Shop's website, you can find details of knitters for hire. Sarah also runs two knitting groups, holds a variety of one-off events such as arm massages and a knitter-friendly pub quiz at the Six Bells just off Mill Road, proving what a sociable and community-based pastime knitting can be!

The Sheep Shop

72 Beche Road, Cambridge CB5 8HU

Tel +44 (0)1223 311268

www.sheepshopcambridge.co.uk

Tues: 10am-2pm, 3pm-7pm (9pm on knit nights)

Weds – Sat: 10am-2pm, 3pm-6pm

Sun & Mon: closed

White House Arts Director: Caroline Amory

Cambridge is the sort of place that however well you think you know it, there always seems to be something interesting and new to discover. This is how it feels on first finding out about White House Arts.

Idyllically located in the Chesterton area of the City on the banks of the Cam, White House Arts offers arts and crafts courses at its independent arts centre. Complementing perfectly this beautiful setting is the ethos of creating a social and therapeutic atmosphere in which people can gain expertise and be creatively inspired.

Courses are run during the day, weekends and evenings and cover a wide range of creative disciplines including ceramics, textiles, mixed media, creative drawing, jewellery, kiln and stained glass, print-making and sculpture, to name just a selection

from the recent programme. White House Arts is a registered charity and all the courses are designed for those age 18 years and over.

All the tutors are artists in their own right with a professional approach to tutoring which, together with small class sizes, ensures all the students gain excellent experience and achieve a sense of accomplishment and satisfaction on completing their finished pieces.

So accomplished do some students become, that they showcase at Open Studios and exhibitions.

And with a significant number of students who return term after term, professionalism combined with a friendly and welcoming approach, appear to be the perfect combination.

White House Arts
72 Fen Road, Cambridge CB4 1UN
Tel: +44 (0)1223 420018
Email: info@whitehousearts.co.uk
www.whitehousearts.co.uk
Reg Charity No. 1142751

CobsBakery Owner: Alan Ackroyd

The smell alone has been known to sell houses, and it was the aroma of freshly baked bread that persuaded Alan Ackroyd to leave his 'proper job' in education and set up his own business – CobsBakery (aka Cambridge Organic Bakery).

His enthusiasm for the humble loaf has not diminished since the first night of baking in 2004 and his mission – to produce fresh, organic, artisan bread – is still the cornerstone of the business. So, as well as the Classic Breads Alan bakes, which include interesting variations such as super seedy, sundried tomato and herb, olive crown and continental fruit loaf, CobsBakery offers a range of loaves called Windmill Breads – featuring products from skilled, local millers. A number of flours are bought from Foster's Mill, just outside Cambridge at Swaffam Prior, who in turn source their grain from local farmers, giving CobsBakery's products true traceability. Delicious breads from this range include sourdough, rye, wholemeal and white spelt varieties. All the breads and rolls are featured on the CobsBakery website and give details about the different ingredients used and dietary notes such as 'free from baker's yeast' for those with sensitivities.

Along with supplying many of the local independent shops, cafés and restaurants, you can buy direct from Alan at the various local Farmers Fayres (when/where are listed on the website). These give him the chance to chat to customers, which allows him to develop his recipes based on their feedback. And if you want to learn his baking secrets why not go along to one of the Bite-sized Bakery workshops, held once a month, so you too can learn all about mixing, kneading and shaping the staff of life!

CobsBakery
7 Robert Davies Court
Nuffield Road
Cambridge CB4 1PT
Tel: +44 (0)1223 241207
Email: info@cobsbakery.com
www.cobsbakery.com

Fresh, organic, artisan bread

cobs BAKERY
Organic
Wholemeal
Bread
800g

Ingredients

www.CobsBakery.com

cobs BAKERY
Country
Malt Loaf
800g

Ingredients

www.CobsBakery.com

Not far from the Cam where it passes Midsummer Common, and situated in the predominantly residential Humberstone Road, is Rowan – a charity and arts centre, set up in 1985, which brings artists and people with learning difficulties together to create the most incredible items of fine artwork and craft.

Many of the pieces made by the students are on display in the gallery and are for sale including beautiful paintings, ceramics, sculptures and carved wooden items such as mirrors – the proceeds from which provide essential income for Rowan, allowing them to continue providing such collaborative opportunities for creativity and self-expression. The quality of the work is so good that the students at Rowan are also commissioned to work on specific pieces and projects, giving them a great sense of self-worth and self-esteem as well as developing their creative skills.

As many of the staff are practicing artists in their own right, it's not surprising that the work produced is of such a high standard. But it goes beyond creativity, as each person is nurtured to help them reach their full personal potential. A visit to Rowan brings this sense of empowerment very much to the forefront, particularly if you are able to see the students at work in one of the four studios.

Rowan is always welcoming to visitors, just get in touch first to make sure someone is there. They also hold regular open events and are part of Cambridge's annual Open Studios – details are on the website or join the mailing list to receive news on what's coming up.

Rowan
40 Humberstone Road, Cambridge CB4 1JG
Tel: +44 (0)1223 566027
Email: info@rowanhumberstone.co.uk
www.rowanhumberstone.co.uk

Not content with having just the one bar in Cambridge, Ashley and Giles from the Lensfield Road Snug took on the Grafton Centre bar in 2009 so they could bring their cocktails to an even larger audience. This is the bigger but younger sister to the Lensfield Road Snug and is the perfect place for resting weary feet after a long day's shopping.

In fact, it's just a great spot whatever you're after. There's a classic breakfast menu for morning sustenance, a tempting all-day food menu and a cocktail list to make your eyes water. Plus just like its sister, this bar offers two for one on their favourite cocktails every day from 3pm until 9pm.

There's even a chic garden area so if the sun does come out you can sit and enjoy your cocktail of choice alfresco style.

Come evening, this bar is perfect for meeting up with friends. There's comfy seating, table service, every drink under the sun and the added bonus that the music is quiet enough to talk over!

The Grafton Snug
170 East Road, Cambridge CB1 1DB
Tel: +44 (0)1223 367888
www.thesnugbar.co.uk

From breakfast and brunch to evening cocktails

25% discount off your food bill with the book

SPECIAL OFFER

The small chain of Snug bars started in Cambridge and are still independently owned and run by local guys, Giles Fry and Ash Moore. They wanted to open a bar company that served great cocktails and fantastic burgers, and so in 2005 they opened their first ever Snug Bar on Lensfield Road.

Nowadays this boutique little spot is cocktail heaven. Their Little Red Book of Cocktails is bursting with everything from hardcore classics, to flighty new concoctions that the expert bar tenders have come up with. You can even choose to share a B.F.G, their biggest cocktail yet at 60oz and served in a giant pineapple. Or if you fancy something but you can't find it on the menu, then just ask and they can shake you something perfect up from scratch. Plus if you head down for happy hour, between 3pm and 9pm daily, and you can even get two for one on the Snug favourite cocktails – that's great local value.

The food is fantastic too, with a menu that includes their homemade Coca Cola ribs, burgers galore and a fine selection of American diner style food. Plus the odd salad and smaller bites for those who fancy a light lunch and all of the food on the menu is made by the kitchen team at the bar, so you know you are indulging in good, handmade grub with your cocktail. All in all this little hidden gem is the ideal spot for food and cocktails come the weekend or a bite of lunch any day of the week.

The Snug Trumpington
67 Lensfield Road
Cambridge CB2 1EN
Tel: +44 (0)1223 367684
www.thesnugbar.co.uk

Great cocktails, great burgers

25% discount off your food bill with the book

SPECIAL OFFER

For an outstanding example of the expertise, knowledge and craftsmanship that blossoms throughout Cambridge, a visit to one particular shop is required. Wood, Wind & Reed is a popular destination for woodwind and brass players from across the country, who come to buy new instruments, have their existing ones repaired and stock up on a range of musical accessories. Situated in Russell Street, which branches off Hills Road, Wood, Wind & Reed is conveniently located only a few minutes' walk away from Cambridge station.

Daniel Bangham began as an instrument maker, specialising in making period clarinets and basset clarinets. He remains in this discipline through his not-for-profit workshops at the Cambridge Woodwind Makers charity, based at the ACE Foundation in Stapleford, which brings the art of instrument making to the wider community. Through Cambridge Woodwind Makers, people can discover the rewarding process of creating their own instrument and hone the skills needed to perfect their musical instrument.

Wood, Wind & Reed has grown continuously since its birth in the early 1980s and now features four testing rooms for people to try out instruments in, a wide range of stock that caters for everyone from the beginner to the professional and an excellent repairs department with a team of expert repairers. All of the staff are active musicians themselves with a wealth of knowledge to offer. This knowledge has helped hundreds of customers to make informed decisions as they choose their new instrument in a friendly, un-pressured environment. Wood, Wind & Reed holds to an ethos of quality in order to ensure that customers truly enjoy playing their instrument.

Wood, Wind & Reed
106 Russell Street
Cambridge CB2 1HU
Tel: +44 (0)1223 500442
www.wwr.co.uk
Tues: 10.30am-8pm
Weds, Thurs, Fri: 9.30am-5.30pm
Sat: 9.30am-4.30pm

South of the city centre and easily found right on the main road is Cambridge's longest-established independent wine merchants – Noel Young Wines. It may be the oldest, but it was started back in 1991 by a very young Noel with a very entrepreneurial streak. Having entered the wine trade at the age of 19, it took only a couple of years before he was running his own business and eyeing up premises to open his first retail outlet.

Hard work and a true passion for wine paid off quickly when in 1995 Noel Young Wines was put firmly on the map by winning the 'Best Small Wine Merchant in the UK' award. Accolades have continued to literally pour in since and all are testament to Noel's ethos of stocking great,

interesting wines that don't necessarily have a huge reputation but if the taste and price is right – he loves buying for his customers to try.

Always forward thinking, Noel treats his online customers to the same high level of service as those visiting the shop. He has also launched a very flexible wine club, loves matching wines to food and gets immersed in local events and wine tastings.

As well as the shop, Noel is a producer too, as co-owner of Magpie Estate in Australia. Initially a small, export-only brand, the quality of the wines has grown over the years and produced award-winning names of its own. So you can imagine the huge knowledge and enthusiasm Noel and the rest of the long-serving team (Daniel, Jamie and Tony) have and which their customers benefit from.

Noel Young Wines

56 High Street, Trumpington
Cambridge CB2 9LS
Tel: +44 (0)1223 566744
Email: admin@nywines.co.uk
www.nywines.co.uk
Mon – Fri: 10am-8pm
Sat: 10am-7pm
Sun: 12pm-2pm

10% off
any
purchase
over £50
with the
book

SPECIAL OFFER

157

Officially in Essex but only 18 miles from Cambridge, the thriving market town of Saffron Walden is buzzing with things to do, things to see and lots of lovely independent shops and traders – some you may recognise from Cambridge too!

Saffron Walden's indie offering includes great boutiques, galleries, cafés, restaurants, antiques and of course market stalls. A market has been held here since 1141 and market days are now every Tuesday and Saturday. Stalls vary from week to week, but amongst the flowers and the fresh fruit you will no doubt find handy household items, fashions, health foods, jewellery, fresh fish and other groceries including locally-sourced organic fruit and veg.

Beyond shopping, Bridge End Gardens is a beautiful setting, with a restored Victorian yew hedge maze that kids will love. There's also an ancient turf maze on the common and a miniature railway, a skate park and the Kids' Museum. History buffs can pay a visit to Audley End House and for art-lovers, the Fry Gallery is not to be missed.

The town is also home to the award-winning independent cinema (Saffron Screen) and a highly acclaimed concert hall due to open to the public in November 2013. It also hosts one of the largest independently organised charity carnivals, so why not join the town for this amazing event in July 2014.

It's easy to find your way, by train from Cambridge to Audley End station (followed by a short bus ride to the town centre), by bus from the Cambridge Bus Station or by a 20 min car journey following the A11 south.

Saffron Shop Local
www.facebook.com/pages/
Saffron-Shop-Local/110250389145374
Tourist Information
www.visitsaffronwalden.gov.uk

Market town with indie Cambridge links

Design Essentials Owner: Wendy Howell

One of the great benefits and satisfactions of shopping independently is the ability to buy something to reflect your individuality. Wendy, founder of Design Essentials is passionate about finding outstanding home accessories and after a long and varied career in retail, has launched her own company to bring a fresh perspective to the home.

Design Essentials offers stylish, contemporary home accessories that are unique and unusual. Often sustainably sourced and all individually chosen by Wendy, many items are handcrafted by local artists and designers, showcasing and supporting their respective talents.

As Design Essentials works so closely with these artisans, your items may be customised to suit your own individual specifications. In fact visiting Wendy's studio space in Saffron Walden becomes a creative, fun experience in itself. Don't forget to leave your own personal message on the big chalk board, it's there for you to share your ideas and even create your own interiors wish list.

For a real exclusive in the home, check out the Italian-designed Pumpkin Light, highlighted by Vogue and only available from Design Essentials. Beautiful, colourful and timeless, once you see them you'll be hard pressed to have just one!

Wendy is always looking for innovative ways of working with others and supporting local shopping. So don't be shy, check out what's new on her website, follow her on Twitter or, for local shopping, on Facebook at Saffron Shop Local.

Design Essentials
Tel: +44 (0)781 3840 402
Email: wendy@designessentials.org.uk
www.designessentials.org.uk
Twitter: @Wendy_Howell1
10 Market Row
Saffron Walden
Essex CB10 1HB

10% off
your
purchase
with this
book

SPECIAL OFFER

161

The Linton Kitchen and The Flower Boutique

Belgian owner, Leen Van den Eede, started her career working as an apprentice at a floral event company based in the famous Waldorf Astoria Hotel in New York. Armed with invaluable training and an ever-growing love for flowers, she moved to the UK, and realised her dream of opening her own shop in 2007.

The Flower Boutique is a haven of floral beauty. Leen's signature style is seasonal, natural and elegant – using only the freshest flowers and foliage shipped directly from the flower markets in Holland.

Well worth the trip out from town, new indie on the block The Linton Kitchen offers city-dwellers and locals alike, a little slice of something special. Set in the chocolate-box High Street of rural Linton in a former butcher's shop, The Kitchen (owned by Gemma Whiting), stocks a wide range of local produce from independent suppliers and producers – using these to create daily sandwiches, lunch specials and scrumptious cakes, topped off with a cup of Cambridge's finest Hot Numbers coffee. Open seven days a week, The Kitchen also has a great selection of lovely foodie gifts.

Not far from Gemma, in the same street, is another fantastic independent – The Flower Boutique.

The Linton Kitchen

30 High Street

Linton CB21 4HS

Tel: +44 (0)1223 894949

www.lintonkitchen.co.uk

Twitter: @LintonKitchen

The Flower Boutique

41 High Street

Linton CB21 4HS

Tel: +44 (0)1223 891740

Email: info@theflowerboutiquelinton.co.uk

www.theflowerboutique.co.uk

For foodies and flower-lovers

THE LINTON KITCHEN

More To Discover

The Linton Kitchen and The Flower Boutique

Before the recent supermarket scandal, the Ashcroft family had already decided to buy their meat from local, independent butchers. For a few years, they even kept their own small herd of cattle and pigs.

Then in 2013, they decided to put their passion to the best effect and opened a family butcher's shop in Linton. Sourcing the meat as locally as possible, from free-ranging, ethically-reared animals – the sausages and burgers are handmade in the shop, and they dry-cure their own bacon and traditionally cure hams. There's also a range of homemade sausage rolls, pies and scotch eggs and a small selection of (mostly home-made) deli products.

More passion, this time for bread, when the Whitby family started Jigsaw Bakery in 2012 – baking at home and selling from the back of a campervan. It was so popular, within six months they had opened a shop on the High Street. There they bake a wide range of British and European breads, including sourdough and rye loaves, using organic flour, without additives, preservatives or improvers. As well as bread, they sell snacks, cakes and drinks, including coffee from local roastery Hot Numbers. They also stock fantastic organic flour from the windmill at Swaffham Prior, organic Fairtrade coffee from London roasters Coffee Plant and other local produce.

Ashcroft & Sons Family Butchers
37 High Street, Linton CB21 4HS
Tel: +44 (0)1223 894224
www.ashcroftfamilybutchers.co.uk

Jigsaw Bakery
113 High Street, Linton CB21 4JT
Tel: +44 (0)1223 890113
www.jigsawbakery.co.uk

Just a few miles outside Cambridge, is the beautifully and sympathetically restored Bury Farm – home to the Bury Farm Music, Arts & Cultural Centre – run by educational charity the ACE Foundation, whose mission is to truly get people participating.

Visiting the internationally renowned centre, with numerous activities and events happening all the time, this desire becomes immediately obvious. A great example of this can be found amongst the converted farm buildings, where space has been created to host an incredible musical instrument making workshop – the Cambridge Woodwind Makers. Under the guidance of expert Daniel Bangham, the aim is to train future generations in the art and craft of woodwind instrument making. Courses at the workshop range from woodwind repair, five-key flute and recorder making.

Every year, a whole host of other stimulating music, art and literature courses are on offer, in the daytime and evenings at Bury Farm. These are open to musicians of all ages from beginners to advanced level – you just need to have a creative mind and a thirst for learning. 'Play days' range from string and flute through to folk, jazz, brass and harp amongst others. There are also creative writing and painting courses all of which are very easy to book and delivered by independent experts of international reputation. With a very friendly and open attitude and the recent addition on-site of a stunning new concert hall, the people and facilities at Bury Farm provide an inspiring space to join in and get creative.

Bury Farm Music, Arts & Cultural Centre
Bury Farm
Stapleford
Cambridge CB22 5BP
Tel: +44 (0)1223 845599
Email: ace@acefoundation.org.uk
www.acefoundation.org.uk

Perched up on a hill just outside Great Shelford, Gog Magog Hills Farm Shop is the ideal spot for picking up your shopping and enjoying a nice slice of cake while you're at it.

The shop, deli and café is run by the Bradford family who have owned the farm since the early 1900s. Brothers Charles and Marcus are at the helm now, with daily help from mum and dad, Lesley and Colin. Add to that the most chirpy, food-loving gaggle of staff around and you've got a farm shop to reckon with.

Service comes with smiles abound and is so knowledgeable that fancy cheese names will greet you as you open the door to the deli. A bunch of first-rate butchers complete the cheery team and they are always on hand to answer questions and suggest cuts for your recipes.

The café serves a tempting menu, including cakes galore and the farm shop's very own award-winning sausage rolls and Scotch eggs, plus a mean cup of Monmouth coffee. It's a great spot for a post-shopping treat or hearty lunch.

The farm shop stocks many local suppliers and takes pride in offering customers the best of the best. So much so in fact, that recent accolades include being voted Observer Food Monthly's runner-up in the UK's Best Independent Retailer Awards, winning five Golds at the Great Taste Awards and reaching the final round of the Butcher's Shop of the Year Awards 2012.

Gog Magog Hills Farm Shop
Heath Farm, Shelford Bottom
Cambridge CB22 3AD
Tel: +44 (0)1223 248352
www.gogmagoghills.com

Foodie heaven

Arriving at the Lynne Strover Gallery, particularly if you have just come from busy central Cambridge, feels like finding a space to breathe – and to be able to do it deeply and properly.

Situated in Fen Ditton's historic High Street, the gallery was created when this former 19th-century school was converted into both a showroom for art and a stunning home for Lynne. The alterations have created a light and airy space – perfect for showing the contemporary British work of the artists she represents. Originally very Cornish in influence, Lynne's reputation for giving great respect to the art as well as the artists, has seen her collection evolve to include work from around 30 established artists from all over the country – including paintings by Maggi Hambling, sculptures by Breon O'Casey, ceramics by Nicholas Rena and rugs by Stella Benjamin. Exhibitions (usually mixed shows) are held throughout the year and, more recently, the gallery has proved a stylish venue for hosting events such as artist talks and recitals.

The one aspect which brings together all the works at the gallery, is Lynne's way of thinking in terms of living spaces. In addition to the intrinsic quality of the individual pieces, the context of interiors in which these are displayed, reflects Lynne's incredible eye for art as well as interior design. Her home is testament to this, having featured in numerous home and style publications.

On a more practical note, there is plenty of available parking, or a cycle ride along the river is an excellent way of visiting. If you want to make a day of it, there is the popular Ancient Shepherds pub nearby and the Crown and Punchbowl in neighbouring Horningsea.

Lynne Strover Gallery
23 High Street, Fen Ditton
Cambridge CB5 8ST
Tel: +44 (0)1223 295264
Email: lynne@strovergallery.co.uk
www.strovergallery.co.uk

Art in the context of interiors

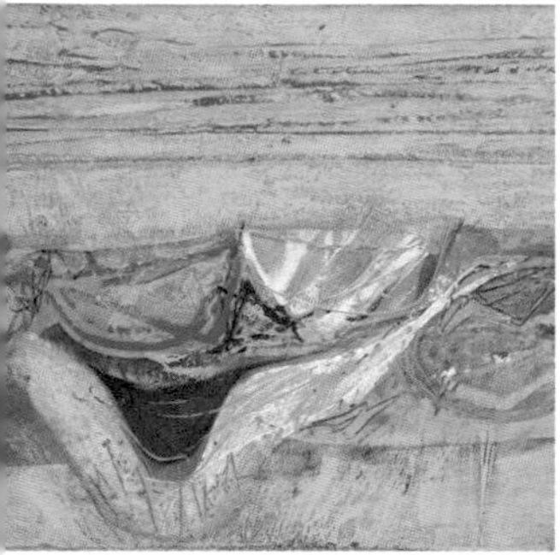
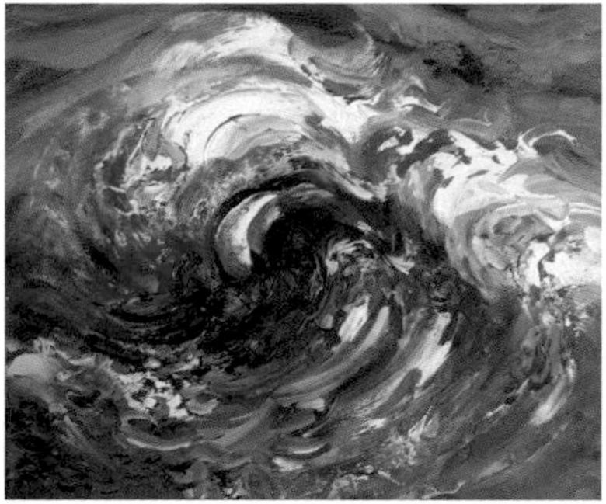

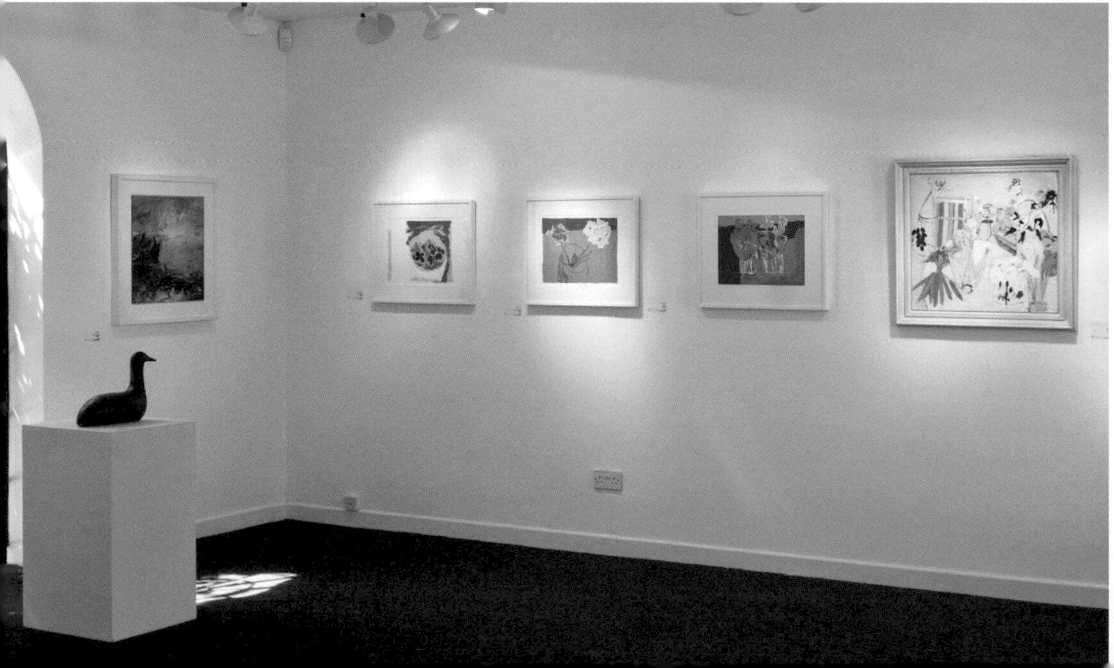

Over Gallery Owner: Helen Taylor

Just ten miles northwest of Cambridge, past the American Cemetery, is the village of Over. Close to the Great Ouse, there are some beautiful river walks right on its doorstep and the highly-ornamented St Mary's Church is well worth a visit too. Now, just along the High Street in the village, is a new destination – Over Gallery.

Opened in December 2012, the Gallery is the most recent reincarnation of a building very central to the life of the village. Built in 1886, this house-come-shop was once the equivalent of a local department store – even selling ice cream made on-site, with ice brought in from Cambridge. When Helen first moved in, the building was in a near derelict state but has now been transformed into a lovely home and of course, the wonderful gallery.

Working closely with a small but growing number of artists, Helen has created a space to showcase contemporary work, much of which is local and inspired by the natural world. Paintings, ceramics, glass, jewellery, sculptures, and hand-crafted furniture by a changing programme of artists including Julia Ball, Jo Tumner, Dafila Scott, Katharina Klug and Althea Braithwaite, all add up to a gallery filled with colour, texture and shape. Exhibitions change regularly throughout the year. There is always a range of studio ceramics, glass and jewellery as well as art cards and wrapping papers – so that the gallery still serves the inhabitants of Over as well as drawing people in for its programme of contemporary art.

Over Gallery
25 High Street, Over
Cambridge CB24 5NB
Tel: +44 (0)1954 230997
Email: helen@overgallery.co.uk
www.overgallery.co.uk

Contemporary art inspired by the natural world

Free greetings card when you spend your first £20 with this book

SPECIAL OFFER

Burwash Manor

27 years ago, Burwash Manor started its transformation from farm to independent retail success, when the first shop was opened on this unique site. It's still a working organic mixed arable and livestock farm, having been run by the same family for over 100 years. Some of the farm's produce is sold in the stunning new Food Hall, asparagus and their free range pork is a particular feast for visitors. The Food Hall also boasts a deli, a very fine butcher's and Italian patisserie.

With lots of free parking, shopping at the converted farm buildings of Burwash Manor is an incredibly relaxing experience: and as it's just two miles from the city centre, it's also an easy bike ride along its own cycle path. Of course, it's not just food you will find there – all of the 15 carefully selected independent shops have something special and different to offer. The very first shop on site sold toys and the most recent 'joiner' is an artists' gallery. The selection of stores offer women's and children's clothing, vintage furniture, fine wines, jewellery, gifts, garden furniture, Persian rugs as well as trees and decorations at Christmas. There's also a great tearoom, a holistic beauty and therapy day spa and plans for an arts and education centre and licensed restaurant. Seriously, what more could you want!

There is more though. Popular educational visits are hosted, based around the signposted farm walks, which anyone can just turn up and use. Every month one or more events are staged, ranging from outdoor theatre to farming celebrations such as Open Farm Sunday and Apple Day, as well as being fun these are a great way to learn about the countryside.

Burwash Manor
New Road, Barton
Cambridge CB23 7EY
Email: info@burwashmanor.com
www.burwashmanor.com

Cambridge Wood Works Owners: David and Catherine

Inspiration comes from many things. In the case of Cambridge Wood Works, the acquisition of a new wood burning stove and the need to find a source of dry, affordable wood was the catalyst for David and Catherine to set up this social enterprise. From this need, they developed the wonderful Cambridge Hotlogs – ideal for woodstoves, they are clean-burning, eco-friendly reclaimed wood briquettes which produce more heat than firewood and less ash.

As well as the Hotlogs, Cambridge Wood Works creates other inspired things from reclaimed timber. For the garden there are log stores, compost bins, picnic tables and herb boxes as well as 'hedgehog hotels', bird and bat boxes! For the home, there are pretty decorative items as well as shelves and occasionally furniture too. You can also specify the exact size of simple items made to order from their range – particularly useful if space is an issue.

The reclaimed scaffold boards used (particularly the older ones), have great character which comes out in all the products and if you are into DIY, you can buy timber here and make your own creations. Cambridge Wood Works also offers a waste wood collection service. There is a charge, but if you are working on a project, it could work out cheaper than hiring a skip and it's guaranteed that 100 percent of the wood is reused or recycled.

The company itself is a Community Interest Company, so they operate for the benefit of the community by providing employment, education and volunteering opportunities and any profits are reinvested in the business, donated to charity or used to help other local community organisations.

Cambridge Wood Works

Unit 9, Penn Farm Studios, Harston Road
Haslingfield, Cambridge CB23 1JZ
Tel: +44 (0)1223 870048
www.cambridgewoodworks.org.uk
Tues – Fri: 10am-4pm and some Saturdays
Closed Sun, Mon and seasonal holidays
Call ahead to check Sat openings.
No card payments, cash/cheque only

10% off
first order
of 4 bags
of Hotlogs

SPECIAL
OFFER

CAMBRIDGE
HOTLOGS

CAMBRIDGE
HOTLOGS

Indies on the web

Cambridgeshire Wine School Owner: Mark Anstead

If you love wine and would like to know why certain wines appeal to you more than others, Cambridgeshire Wine School is for you. Through a range of relaxed evening tastings and Saturday courses, you can learn how wines from different regions of the world are likely to vary in taste – helpful whenever you buy wine.

With a background in journalism and celebrity interviewing, coupled with a love of wine and food, Mark combines natural communication skills with his professional wine qualifications to offer courses and tastings that are fun as well as informative. His goal is to give people 'a mental map' for choosing wine.

Cambridge is a great place for Mark to run wine courses. With a number of really strong independent wine sellers (though supermarket wines are also on the menu) and some great venues (he mainly uses The Cambridge Brew House, 12a Club and Cambridge City Hotel) he is able to offer an all-round enjoyable experience.

Mark's courses and tastings are aimed at all levels of experience and knowledge so there is no need to feel intimidated. There is an 8-week 'World of Wine Tour' you can block book for a £30 saving, single evening tastings themed around particular regions and Saturday Wine Courses offering a leisurely tasting of 13 wines with a two-course lunch and champagne included in the price. You can book social evenings for private and business groups and buy gift vouchers for a birthday and Christmas that never expire! Plus there are professional WSET qualifications suitable for people working in hotels, bars and restaurants or anyone who just wants to further their personal interest in wine.

Cambridgeshire Wine School
Tel: +44 (0)1223 655391
Mobile: +44 (0)7989 606447
Email: info@cambridgeshirewineschool.com
www.cambridgeshirewineschool.com

Helping you choose wine more easily

Checkpoint Reality comes from the unofficial inscription, originally painted sometime in the 1970s, on the lamp-post in the middle of Parker's Piece. There are a few theories (usually involving students!) about its meaning, but whatever the original source, it represents individuality and has become part of what makes Cambridge special.

On her arrival from Australia to study in 2003, it was exactly this quirky side of Cambridge Anita fell in love with. Being immensely proud of the place she now lives in and inspired by the less obvious cityscapes she sees, Anita decided to capture these images and create her own range of Cambridge T-shirts, kids' clothes, tea towels, bags and cards.

A gift of a beautiful 1959 Raleigh means getting out and about taking photographs is a huge source of fun as well as creativity and the 'Ol Girl' as the bike is fondly known, can even be seen cropping up in some of Anita's designs. Working from home, she screen-prints by hand to transfer her images to her range. The bags, tea towels and T-shirts are all made using 100 percent cotton and Anita chooses suppliers carefully both for their high-quality material as well as the gorgeous colours they can provide for her clothing items.

As well as the Checkpoint Reality website, Anita has a stall at the main Cambridge Sunday market and also takes part in local events such as the Mill Road Winter Fair and if you live in Cambridge, Anita and the 'Ol Girl' will deliver your order free!

Checkpoint Reality
Tel: +44 (0)1223 562283
www.checkpointreality.co.uk
www.facebook.com/CheckpointReality
Twitter: @CheckpointR

Hand-printed Cambridge designs

Inder and Nick moved from London to Cambridge in 2010 and have quickly established their Indian catering business – Inder's Kitchen – as a take-away with a real difference, by showing the diverse range of dishes and flavours that Indian cuisine really has to offer.

The dishes cooked in Inder's Kitchen are all prepared true to traditional Indian recipes – using fresh locally-sourced ingredients and spices that Inder and her team grind and blend themselves. The seasonal menus offer starters that are based on typical Indian street foods, as well as a range of curries, side dishes and pickles which are cooked in homes across India. In the category of Best Takeaway/ Street Food, Inder's Kitchen was nominated as one of just three national finalists in the BBC Food and Farming Awards in 2012.

Inder and the team have also come up with a range of ways to enjoy this authentic culinary experience. Relish Indian home cooking in the comfort of your own home with the free delivery service to all areas of Cambridge, Trumpington, Granchester, Girton, Teversham, Fen Ditton, the Shelfords and Stapleford. Or for smaller gatherings, Inder produces a range of great value curries and canapés that can simply be popped in the oven before you and your guests want to eat. For larger parties or office events, a full catering service is also available. Deliciously alternative to the usual boring sandwiches and pizzas that often accompany office meetings, treat yourself instead to snacks such as samosas, Indian style wraps, lentil cakes and more.

Inder's Kitchen
43 Clifton Road
Cambridge CB1 7ED
Tel: +44 (0)1223 211333
Email: info@inderskitchen.com
www.inderskitchen.com
Tues – Fri: 12pm-10pm (last orders)
Sat & Sun: 5pm-10pm (last orders)

Melanie Driver Landscape & Garden Design

From small town gardens to large estates, Melanie Driver has helped people visualise the potential of the spaces they have and transform them into beautiful living areas - integrating the house into the garden and the garden into the landscape.

With a background in fine art and design and a love of landscape and horticulture, Melanie first started a career in garden design by retraining in 2001 and setting up her own company. Originally living and working in Dorset, a move to Cambridge now means we can benefit from her creativity and knowledge too.

Melanie has created over 100 beautiful gardens for her private residential clients and architects, as well as for major shows such as the Hampton Court Flower Show. Her work combines beautiful craftsmanship with intelligent planting and she finds the process of collaborating with clients as inspiring as working with colour, texture and form. An initial consultation allows her to discover how the space is to be used and explore ideas. She also provides a consultation-only service.

Moving on with a project, Melanie conducts a detailed site analysis then uses specialist CAD drawing tools to produce accurate scaled drawings. Perspective views can also be produced which are a great help to visualise the finished design.

Of course when it comes to the actual 'build' Melanie is in her element. Managing the whole process including liaising with other professionals, Melanie's passion for her work ensures every garden brings the utmost pleasure to her clients. Lucky Cambridge!

Melanie Driver
Tel: +44 (0)7866 692541
Email: studio@melaniedriver.co.uk
www.melaniedriver.co.uk

Creating beautiful, living spaces

Events

For one night a year, in the run-up to Christmas, the Unitarian Church Hall in Victoria Street near Christ's Pieces Park, is magically transformed with lanterns and fairy lights as a specially selected group of local artists and designer/makers gather to exhibit their work.

This particular Christmas story began in 2008, when Jo Tunmer – a local painter and printmaker – held a one-off artists event at her house. The show was a huge success and the following year Jo had secured larger premises and Cambridge Christmas moved to its new home at the Church Hall.

Due to limited space, exhibitors are selected by invitation only, ensuring the highest quality of work is on show. For the 2013 event (being held on Monday 25th November 1pm to 8.30pm) there will be prints and cards from Jo Tunmer Ltd, Alison Hullyer and Roxana de Rond, jewellery from Lauren Rowden and Bek Genery, ceramics by Rachel Dormor, Amanda MacPhail and Katharina Klug, unique recycled bags and accessories by QHERE, wire sculpture by Rhiannon Thomas, handmade books by Edel Hopkin, glass by Alison Tait, unique fine art lollipops by Joali, books from children's illustrator Nicola Killen and amazing book sculptures by Justin Rowe.

Although the show has become bigger, the ethos of the event remains the same – to provide a place where local artists and crafts professionals can display their work in a warm and personal environment. So while browsing for gifts and chatting to the exhibitors, you can enjoy seasonal offerings of home-made mince pies and mulled cider. It's the perfect environment to purchase Christmas presents (or personal treats!), that you just wouldn't find anywhere else.

Cambridge Christmas
Email: info@cambridgechristmas.com
www.cambridgechristmas.com

Cambridge Folk Festival

Set in the beautiful parkland setting of Cherry Hinton Hall, Cambridge Folk Festival is one of the highlights of the city's calendar. Attracting 14,000 people across four days in late July, the Festival draws on its unrivalled 49-year musical heritage, combining it with the brand new, quirky, up-and-coming and unsung, to create a unique event each year.

It began in autumn 1964, when Cambridge City Council decided to hold a music festival the next summer and asked Ken Woollard, a local firefighter and socialist political activist, to help organise it. Woollard had been inspired by a documentary – 'Jazz On A Summer's Day', about the 1958 Newport Jazz Festival. On the very first Festival bill, squeezed in as a late addition, was a young Paul Simon who had just released 'I Am A Rock'. The festival's popularity quickly grew, evolving over the years into one of the most well-loved and best regarded of its kind.

Today it features five stages – Main Stage, Stage 2, Club Tent, The Den and the latest delightful tiny gem of a stage, The People's Front Room. Festival artists over the years have included Jake Bugg, Laura Marling, Richard Thompson, Toots and The Maytals, Newton Faulkener, Jimmy Cliff, Mary Chapin Carpenter, Bellowhead, Gillian Welch, Mumford and Sons, The Staves, Lucy Rose, Robert Cray, Christy Moore, Kate Rusby, Nanci Griffith, The Unthanks, Seasick Steve, Imelda May, Femi Kuti, Seth Lakeman, Nic Jones and many others.

Cambridge Folk Festival turns 50 in 2014, a milestone in a history marked by its true originality and unique ability to both celebrate the past and look to the future.

Cambridge Folk Festival

Tel: +44 (0)1223 457555
Email: admin.cornex@cambridge.gov.uk
www.cambridgefolkfestival.co.uk

Perahia (piano), Andreas Scholl (counter-tenor), Pekka Kuusisto (electric violin), the Nash Ensemble, Academy of St Martin in the Fields and Britten Sinfonia, a major education project involving hundreds of young singers across the county and an amazing Virtual Choir of nearly 4,000 singers from 76 countries projected onto the Senate House in the city centre.

Many stunning buildings across the city are home to the Festival's programme of concerts such as King's College Chapel, the Divinity School opposite St John's College, West Road Concert Hall, the Corn Exchange and the Mumford Theatre at Anglia Ruskin University.

In November 2012, the first Cambridge Music Festival (CMF) under its new director Justin Lee, was a great success story. CMF attracted national press coverage as well as audiences and young people from across the region to a wide variety of orchestral, choral and chamber concerts, education projects and a major sound and light projection onto the street-side of King's College Chapel.

November 2013 promises the same mix of music, education and technology – with world-class artists including Nigel Kennedy (violin), Murray

Cambridge Music Festival
Tel: +44 (0)1223 357851
Email: info@cammusic.co.uk
www.cammusic.co.uk

Murray Perahia
Piano

Nigel Kennedy
Violin

Eric Whitacre's Virtual Choir

Now in its twelfth year, Cambridge Wordfest has a firm place on the Cambridge cultural calendar. In addition to staging two literary festivals each year – April and November/December – it hosts a series of individual events throughout the year.

Over the years Wordfest has hosted hundreds of writers including literary luminaries such as Ian McEwan, Jeanette Winterson, Margaret Drabble, Chimamanda Ngozi Adichie, Zadie Smith and Graham Swift; politicians including Michael Portillo, Tony Benn and Jack Straw; broadcasters Andrew Marr, Kate Adie and Nick Robinson; comedians including Dawn French, Jeremy Hardy and Sandi Toksvig; poetry from Carol Ann Duffy, Andrew Motion, John Hegley; the burgeoning children's festival has hosted many of our best writers for children including Michael Morpurgo, Jacqueline Wilson and Francesca Simon.

Cambridge is a great place for a literary festival, with endless interesting and beautiful venues and Wordfest uses many of them. You might find yourself in the splendour of the Cambridge Union Chamber or the hidden gem which is the Winstanley Lecture Theatre or the wonderfully intimate ADC Theatre. It also has a host of talented residents – writers, historians and academics who the festival regularly invites to speak including Ali Smith, Robert Macfarlane, Anna Whitelock, David Reynolds, Chris Clarke, Gillian Beer, Sophie Hannah and Rowan Pelling.

But although the festival has grown so successfully, Cambridge Wordfest has managed to retain its initial intimacy and vivacity and continues to delight its festival-goers by bringing the best in new and established writers to the historic and beautiful city.

Cambridge Wordfest
Festival Office
7 Downing Place, Cambridge, CB2 3EL
Tel: +44 (0)1223 515335
Email: admin@cambridgewordfest.co.uk
www.cambridgewordfest.co.uk

Mill Road Winter Fair

The Mill Road Winter Fair celebrates the quirky community spirit and multiculturalism that make this road so special. Always held on the first Saturday in December, it's an important event in the seasonal calendar – bringing many thousands of people to the area, raising the profile of Mill Road, increasing awareness of its many and diverse businesses and community groups and generally providing a colourful and fun-filled time for visitors.

With the road closed between East Road and Coleridge Road, visitors to the fair can stroll along the street and see the amazing variety of what is on offer. Crammed full of independent shops, Mill Road is truly diverse, both in what can be found for sale or to eat and in terms of who is selling or preparing it. Chinese and Korean restaurants and supermarkets, cyber cafés and coffee houses, Indian restaurants, an Italian delicatessen, North African, Adriatic and Turkish restaurants and shops selling organic and locally-produced food and other wears sit alongside antique shops, bookshops, bike shops, a butcher's, a baker's and there's probably even a candlestick-maker!

As well as the variety of shops, the fair hosts a food fair, art show and craft stalls and sees street performers congregate to entertain the public. Musicians, dancers and other artists all gather to perform along the road and in marquees, pubs and clubs. Truly something for everyone!

Mill Road Winter Fair
C/O The Post Office, 100A Mill Road
Cambridge CB1 2BD
Tel: +44 (0)7982 810343
Email: info@millroadwinterfair.org
www.millroadwinterfair.org

A perfect mixture of organised spontaneity!

Indie index A-Z